BEATTY'S RAILWAY

BEATTY'S RAILWAY

PHILIP MARSH

NEW CHERWELL PRESS · OXFORD

First published in Great Britain 2000
by New Cherwell Press
7 Mount Street, Oxford OX2 6DH
Copyright © estate of Philip Marsh 2000
ISBN 1 900312 45 X

Cover design by Malvin Van Gelderen
Printed by Biddles, King's Lynn

To my wife

JANE

Whatever you can do or dream you can, begin it.
Boldness has genius, power and magic in it.

Goethe

PREFACE

The Crimean railway brought the cutting edge technology and boundless confidence of mid-Victorian engineering to the service of the state. By enabling the Army to move supplies, ammunition, artillery and even buildings up to the camp and the front line, it enabled the British to continue the siege of Sebastopol. In a war that was always short of heroes, James Beatty stands out. In this book he is given his due, as a resourceful railway pioneer and as a brave man.

Professor Andrew Lambert
Department of War Studies,
King's College,
London.

CONTENTS

Page

Foreword

1 A Great Idea: *Thursday, 23rd November 1854*   1

2 A Promise and a Half: *Friday, 1st December*   14

3 No Shrinking Violets: *Saturday, 2nd December*   25

4 The Best Passport: *Monday, 4th December*   37

5 Some Departures: *Wednesday, 13th December*   45

6 The Sublime Porte: *26th December*   58

7 A Miserly Little Town: *18th January 1855*   71

8 Nightmare Journeys: *19th January*   76

9 Confrontations: *20th January*   82

10 New Faces—New Problems: *21st January*   92

11 The Navvies! *2nd February*   102

12 Build Up and Break Out: *8th February*   109

13 Up and Running: *16th February*   119

14 Opening Day: *23rd February*   137

15 Success—and a Spill: *26th March*   157

16 Bombardments: *7th April*   169

17 Question time in Heraclea: *May*   180

18 Disarray and Dispersals: *July*   190

19 Fall of the Fortress: *8th September*   200

20 The Homeward Run: *25th November*   207

21 The End of a Dream: *11th March 1856*   216

     Afterword   226

     Acknowledgements   233

     Sources   235

FOREWORD
18th February 1856

The two doctors have just left my bedroom—a short visit; probably one of the last; Sarah, white-faced, showing them downstairs to our front door. Brief examination, muttered conversation on landing: then, what I'd been half expecting for weeks—a death sentence. Aneurysm, they said, almost certainly of the aorta. At most, only a few weeks to live: I should place myself in the hands of the Almighty; put my affairs in order. Amen!

My state, both physicians agree, has been caused by internal injuries from accident on Crimean railway—the very line from Balaklava to Sebastopol that I had built with a 580-strong workforce under appalling conditions last year.

Propped up in bed to make breathing just possible, I am numbed by what this verdict will mean for my dearest Sarah and our four chicks. Even now, though, faced with this crisis, I feel I must finish the last pages of my story of that railway—'Beatty's Railway', as my friend Russell of *The Times* termed it—as a small memorial for my young family who will never now hear the story from my lips.

My throat and left arm are unbearably swollen, but I can still just grip a pencil in the right hand. Bless the premonition that spurred me on to start the book while I was a sick passenger on the homebound steamer, *Thames*, coaling at Constantinople!

Then, every aspect of my year-long expedition to the Crimea was vivid in my mind—details crowding in, prompted by diary entries, reports to my firm in London, talks with Lord Raglan and other service chiefs. Memories, too, of my letters home, and Sarah's to me with family news that held me steady in dark times.

I am still—even now—kept abreast of developments through regular reports from my friend and faithful colleague, Donald Campbell, who took over as engineer-in-chief when I left Balaklava.

I *will*, DV, finish the tale now—the story of a railway that won the war.

James Beatty
13 Blomfield Terrace,
Paddington,
London.

1

A GREAT IDEA

Thursday 23rd November 1854

'Good morning, Beatty; thank you for coming so quickly.' After a vigorous handshake, Mr. Peto led me briskly across the hall of his elegant Westminster house to his private study. 'Edward Betts has just arrived,' he added, 'so we can get straight down to business.' As we entered the room he took my overcoat and muffler; I was glad to see a fire burning in the grate for the weather outside was icy. Betts and I nodded to each other as we sat down, silently watching our host who, uncharacteristically, was pacing the carpet in front of us.

Mr. Samuel Morton Peto, senior partner of Peto, Brassey and Betts, the country's largest contractors, and Whig MP for Norwich for the past nine years, was normally a highly reserved man, but now his face was flushed and animated and his voice had a strong ring. Despite the habitual stiffness of his tall figure he was clearly in the grip of extreme excitement. Suddenly he stopped, gripped the back of a chair and looked down piercingly at us.

'I only arrived home from my Danish trip yesterday,' he said, 'but I needed to talk to the two of you as soon as possible—hence the telegrams. The fact is, gentlemen, I have had an idea—a great idea—that I believe could utterly transform the course of our disastrous war in the Crimea...'

On the morning he sailed, he told us, the Danish foreign minister had shown him, confidentially, a secret report he had just received from Constantinople—its news, he assured him, wouldn't yet have reached London. It was a warning of imminent disaster for the British Army. An unprecedented hurricane, accompanied by sleet and snow from the north, had struck the Crimean peninsula, turning the only road leading from the port of Balaklava into a

1

gigantic quagmire. Nothing could be moved up to the British front lines on the central plateau facing Sebastopol except on the backs of soldiers who were daily getting weaker, and fewer, as cholera and typhus tightened their grip.

'Something has to be done at once, and we're going to do it,' declared Mr. Peto. Thus began, at 10 am precisely on that Wednesday, 23rd November 1854, the most momentous meeting I had taken part in since joining the firm as chief engineer of the new Eastern Counties Railway twelve years before. It was a meeting that would completely change my life.

Silence suddenly fell and we sat motionless as if in some timeless painting, Then came the quick, forthright tones of Edward Ladd Betts, who was always on the most comfortable of terms with Mr. Peto, as brother-in-law as well as junior partner.

'Exactly what is this great idea of yours, Sam?'

'I'm just about to explain, Edward,' replied Mr. Peto, a trifle sharply. Then, recollecting himself, and with a conciliatory smile, he too sat down and continued his story. The idea had actually occurred to him during his homeward voyage, after being presented with the Order of the Danebrog by Frederick VII in recognition of the firm's completion in record time of Denmark's new Jutland-Schleswig railway. After the ceremony, the King and he had travelled together along the line, from the old frontier fortress of Rensburg to Tonning on the coast.

He had been greatly struck by the commercial possibilities of such a link between hinterland and port.

'Suddenly, Balaklava came into my mind,' continued Peto. 'Why not, I thought, a railway from *that* tiny port to the front lines on the heights above Sebastopol, to carry ammunition and supplies up to our troops? Then I thought: why shouldn't *our* firm offer to build that line... build it *now*, *at cost*, no profit to us? There and then, I determined to do it.'

'That's quite first-class,' cried Betts spontaneously.

'And us to control the whole enterprise?' I put in.

'Indeed, indeed, Beatty,' said Mr. Peto. 'That will be absolutely essential for success.'

As soon as his ship moored at Lowestoft, Mr. Peto had made straight for Mr. Brassey's country residence to consult with him. To his delight—and, he confessed, amazement—the idea was wholeheartedly welcomed by his old friend and partner who immediately pledged support—'in every way, every day till we get the armada off.' Looking straight at us, Mr. Peto repeated his friend's final words as they parted that night: 'The time is right, Sam. You must push it through: it is your national duty.'

'So,' said Mr. Peto, jumping to his feet and beginning his restless pacing again, 'now you understand why I have called you two in. I want your help urgently to prepare a plan I can put to the Secretary for War, the Duke of Newcastle.'

What he had required was, he emphasized, a cast-iron proposition. Every facet of it to be examined in minute detail and the whole scheme fully worked out, with a time-table for each phase of the operation—and costed, too, he had added, almost as an after-thought.

I remember how we had both gazed at him, dumbfounded, Then the irrepressible Betts burst out: 'And you expect all this by tomorrow?'

I laughed: Betts' comment was not so much a question as a simple statement of fact. We were both only too familiar with demands of a sweeping nature from the senior partner.

Mr. Peto joined in the laughter, and did his best to reassure us. Our plan must, of course, be comprehensive and meticulously thought through; yet, he insisted, he didn't intend to tie our hands. Still, he had to admit that speed was the vital factor: he had to have our plan within four days—by Tuesday, 28th November, in fact.

All the firm's resources were at our disposal: 'Use our office manager, Deacon, and any of the staff. Call on Mr. Brassey and me; we'll be somewhere around.'

'But work, work, I beg you,' he concluded earnestly, 'harder than either of you have ever worked before, even in Canada. Edward, you're our man for the supply side; Beatty, you must pick the workforce. We'll want you as engineer-in-chief in the Crimea, if all goes well. Now, I must get over to the House: there's serious work for me to do there. Good luck to you both—and God bless you!'

These last remarks had brought us instantaneously to our feet. As the study door closed behind a flying Mr. Peto, Betts and I looked at each other, dazed. Then, gripping my arm he said quietly: 'You heard what he wants, Beatty: we'd better commandeer the boardroom and get Deacon to bring coffee.'

* * * * * * *

Until that moment, thoughts of the war had been fairly remote from my mind. Work at head office had settled into a steady daily routine, and there was little comment among us about the Campaign apart from grumbles about its generally dampening effect on our business prospects, and casual gossip about friends at the front.

It was a far cry from the day when I had been urgently recalled from Nova Scotia by the firm, and arrived at Southampton at the end of March with my young family, staff and gangs of men. War against Russia had been declared on the very day we docked, and the general reaction seemed to be one of jubilation. Troops on their way to embarkation had been cheered through the streets: church bells were rung. The sounds had jarred on me and my party.

We had felt sick at heart at having been forced to abandon a project that had totally engaged our energies for the best part of eight months. In that time, we had completely laid out the first railway routes in the Province, as part of the projected Grand Canadian Trunk network designed to reach the vast untapped resources of the interior. The last stage had been accomplished in the teeth of a savage winter, with the thermometer at -20°F and three feet of snow on the forest floor. Yet the sun shone steadily from a pale blue sky, and we had adapted well enough to life under canvas on an unrelieved diet of salt pork and hard biscuit. And we had come through unscathed: no one in any of my scattered parties was even hospitalized with frostbite.

In my mind this task was just the first stage in what I had hoped 1854 would prove to be for me—a year of destiny. The next step would have been directing the actual construction of the lines themselves. After that—well, at thirty-four years of age, anything was possible! To be summarily brought back to England had been a body blow, even though I could understand my firm's anxieties about capital expenditure in Canada as war clouds darkened over Europe.

Only one member of my family was actually out in the Crimea—Ethelbert Blake—one of Sarah's cousins, who was serving as a surgeon with his artillery regiment. During all the months of campaigning, he had sent just one letter to his parents in Ireland, who, typically, had taken that as a token that all was still well with him.

Other than personal comments in officers' letters, which were frequently out of date, all that we at home had to go on were rumours (often contradictory), statements in Parliament (confused) and items gleaned from dispatches by special correspondents with our army in the field, most notably W. H. Russell of *The Times*.

No wonder there was a general feeling of bewilderment. Once the initial excitement had worn off, none of us knew quite what to make of the state of affairs in the Crimea. It was hard enough to fathom exactly why the war had begun and what Britain was really fighting for. It was said to have had something to do with a quarrel between the Latin Church and Greek Orthodox monks over rights and privileges in the Holy Places of Jerusalem; something, as well, to do with the Czar of Russia's demands on Turkey and his lust for territory, which fed deep suspicions among the major European powers; something also—and the most likely—to do with Emperor Napoleon III's manoeuvring to bolster his position by nailing his shaky tricolour to England's strong masthead. A typical piece of Gallic cheek! No wonder it was reported that Lord Raglan, the commander-in-chief, habitually referred to our French allies as 'the enemy'—a hark back to the days of Waterloo when he had served on Wellington's staff and had his right arm taken off by a ball.

In the end, whatever the root causes may have been and despite all misgivings, Allied armies had marched east in strength to the defence of a Turkish Sultan! Most of us still felt that our English politicians had everything still to do to prove they were actually in control of events, but everyone was profoundly certain that our soldiers and sailors would emerge valiant and victorious.

But, as the bitter Crimean winter had deepened, folk's apprehensions had sharpened; a groundswell of criticism was fed by a rising torrent of letters from men at the front, seemingly powerless in their daily struggle for existence.

What then, I began to wonder, could honestly be made of the much-trumpeted 'successes' of Alma, Balaklava and Inkerman—bloody battles all of them? All that had ultimately shone through was the endurance and courage of ordinary soldiers—a brilliance crowned by the supreme valour of that single charge which had seen an unflinching Light Brigade swept away in a morning.

Victory seemed a mocking mirage; cholera and typhus were the daily reality. That, and the loss of irreplaceable troops in unchronicled actions; of sentries frozen to death on night piquet; of the wounded perishing in agony in their thousands through military mismanagement and medical neglect.

Meanwhile, defying bombardment, Russia's great fortress of Sebastopol still stood unconquered, its shadow stretching far beyond the Black Sea.

* * * * * * *

Once inside the boardroom, Betts and I had, out of habit, taken up station on either side of the long mahogany table. Then the tension of the occasion had dramatically dissolved into smiles: impulsively we leaned forward and warmly shook hands across the polished surface.

There was in truth little enough to smile about: we had been set the most daunting challenge—to produce in four days a plan for building a railway across uncharted enemy territory, thousands of miles from our only industrial base. We had to determine what plant and materials would be required, estimate their cost and then find and mobilize a workforce.

Deacon had provided us with pens, pencils and rulers in plenty, and foolscap paper by the ream. What we did not have was a single map of the Crimean Peninsula!

I made it my first job to track down copies of every available civilian map in London. That took surprisingly little time: there was only a handful, and those merely reprints of thirty-five-year-old

Russian military surveys—one, I was amused to note, with a flattering dedication to our Sovereign, Queen Victoria. All suffered from the same major defect: there were no contour markings. Even the largest-scale maps recorded little topographical detail—only a few towns, post roads, woods, vineyards and scattered water wells.

I did unearth one sketchy map of the whole peninsula in a Black Sea handbook, published on 17th February 1854 by James Wyld, the Royal Geographer, whose preface expressed his modest hope that the notes would be of interest 'not only to the British public but also useful to those prosecuting the war.'

In the face of such sparse factual evidence it was clear that our sole sources of information about the terrain and its geographical and climatic characteristics lay in newspaper reports and memories of officers returning from the front. To some extent Betts and I could supplement these with our own experiences of working overseas in rugged country.

One remark that had particularly registered in Betts' mind was, he said, a comment made to him a few days earlier at his club by a fellow member—Sir George de Lacy Evans, commander of Second Division, who was home on sick leave. His over-riding memory of the Crimea had, he recounted grimly, been of the seemingly endless succession of wintry rainstorms that instantly turned the light soil of the limestone plateau and the plain into a nightmare of glutinous mud, obliterating all tracks and isolating the few tents still standing.

There was nothing for it but to make a start with whatever facts we had, and I couldn't have had a more congenial collaborator than Edward Ladd Betts with whom I had worked for many years on railway contracts in England and Canada. Although at thirty-nine he was five years older than me, our temperaments and working methods were alike, and I had always found his sense of humour highly relaxing at moments of tension.

Like Mr. Peto, he had as a boy been apprenticed to a builder, and had built his first lighthouse under the direction of his father at Beaumaris in North Wales at the age of nineteen, one year before he married Mr. Peto's youngest sister. From then on, his career had been almost wholly concerned with railways. His thoroughness was a by-word in the industry: he was reputed to sleep only four hours a night! That I could well believe; without such discipline he could never have coped with the avalanche of paper concerning company projects that passed daily across his desk.

So began a memorable four-day stint of debate, calculation, list building—kite flying even! We were stalwartly supported throughout by 'Boy' Deacon, who had joined Mr. Peto at the age of fifteen, and who supplied us with snacks at intervals and, at all hours, with statistics, estimates and invaluable staff suggestions. Following our orders, Betts and I methodically weighed up every aspect of the expedition, from plant, rails, general and medical supplies to size and number of ships needed to transport everything to Balaklava in speediest time. The only matter we didn't need to consider for our new corps was rations; those would be the responsibility of the Commissary-General's department on the spot.

We were in immediate agreement on the need for horse-drawn wagons in the early build-up of the line, and plumped for an initial contingent of thirty-five shire horses (and horsemaster), complete with sets of harness, tackle and fodder, and sectional stables. We made provision in the estimates, too, for the purchase of locomotives for long-term haulage once the hastily-constructed rail beds had been strengthened and consolidated.

Our talk had flowed freely, non-stop: then suddenly it came to a halt. It was at the end of a particularly exhausting day that Betts broached the question of manpower—the subject that had been foremost in my thoughts from the moment when Mr. Peto had put on my shoulders responsibility for recruiting the workforce. It was a difficult equation to balance—a small staff of officers with a great mass of navvies, gangers and skilled craftsmen all combining to work together under pressure in a battlefield situation! No wonder I kept pondering the problem.

Betts' approach had struck me as bordering on the flippant. 'I think three hundred men should be all right, eh, Beatty?' he asked, adding: 'We really must think of the cost. Besides, navvies and their ilk are a right handful at the best of times, and they'll be a long way from home—not that many have much of a home to remember.'

His cool tone suddenly irritated me; I sensed in his words a not too subtle attempt to exert control over an area which was genuinely my province. I lost my temper: 'Look here, Betts,' I said, shortly, 'if that's the best suggestion you can offer, please don't bother to say anything more. Three hundred men is a ludicrous number—and you know it. I refuse to discuss the matter further now. We'll talk in the morning.' With that, I got up and left the room, leaving Betts sitting in awkward silence.

A sour and sorry end to an otherwise fruitful day. Yet so much— in fact, everything—hung on getting the manpower calculations right. As I strode through the echoing streets my irritation ebbed, but by the time I reached home I felt utterly drained. Still, the manpower question would have to be settled now, once and for all. Sarah put up with my poor attempt at conversation over supper. Afterwards, I pushed the cloth aside and settled down solidly to thrashing out the whole question from first principles. By the time I had finished in the early hours, the figures were fairly dancing in front of my eyes, but I was convinced that I had at last reached the right decisions.

Even if the final total were to prove thrice the figure tossed up so nonchalantly into the air by Betts, that was quite beside the point. Once ashore at Balaklava, our workforce would need to be completely self-sufficient, in skills and in numbers. There would be no chance of instant reinforcements should calamity befall.

Satisfied, I went to bed, to find Sarah peacefully sleeping.

As I approached 9 Great George Street the next morning at my usual brisk pace I found I was bracing myself for a frosty encounter. However, one glance at Betts' face reassured me: he too had been reflecting deeply on the situation, as his first words showed. Crossing the boardroom, he held out his hand: 'I apologise for my ill chosen words last evening, Beatty,' he said. 'The composition of the workforce is, of course, entirely a matter for you.' With that, we both sat down and I paged him a duplicate set of my figures which he scanned with close attention, nodding approval once or twice.

'I confess it took hours last night to get the balance right,' I said, 'and I kept very much in mind your caution about navvies being a handful. They certainly can be all of that; I know from bitter experience what havoc even one small unruly gang can cause. But troublesome or not, they're the very core of our plan. I just hope I can hand-pick the best of whatever bunch shows up, and instill some rudiments of discipline into them. It's a tall order, I grant you, but there's no alternative.

'A force of a thousand would no doubt see us through every contingency, but that would mean trebling labour costs and putting up staff numbers. My aim is to run a tight unit with a small, first-class staff. So, as you can see from my paper, I'm taking an optimistic view of possible casualties and plumping for a workforce of just over half that number—five hundred and fifty navvies and craftsmen, and a total staff strength of twenty-eight, which has to include not only assistant engineers, surveyors and timekeepers, but also surgeons and nurses, cashiers and scripture readers.'

To my relief, Betts gave the list unqualified support. 'Just one thing,' he added. 'Do pay particular attention to choice of gangers: they can make or break contracts.' He immediately offered to supply a chief cashier and three assistants from head office, adding with a grin that he was sure Mr. Peto, as a devout Baptist, would be happy to recommend a couple of readers, together with a personal gift of Bibles and books for the men. Such was his invariable custom on all contracts.

Our last working day together—Monday, 27th November—came on us in a rush. That was the last chance to re-examine all elements of our scheme before preparing a formal plan for scrutiny by Mr. Peto and Mr. Brassey the following morning.

Our over-riding aim had been to provide a rail network with the capability to supply our artillery, siege trains and front-line infantry with sufficient shot, shell and ancillary material to make continuous bombardment of Sebastopol possible—indefinitely.

We were proposing double-track running from Balaklava across the plain, with single track on all other stretches. The most difficult engineering problem would undoubtedly be dealing with the line of ascent to the 660 ft. summit. Only a survey on the spot could reveal just how severe the gradient would prove, but theoretically we considered it could be done by using stationary engines and winding gear. Once on the plateau, all British batteries, as well as French and Turkish positions, would be served by single track, with a spur to the Commissariat depot near headquarters.

Writing out the plan brought all our objectives into sharp focus. Basically, we had gone for the old option—surprise. First, the swiftest possible assembly of men and materials; second, all-out construction on arrival at the harbour, with day and night working in all conditions.

Possibly this went beyond our initial remit, and might well be thought presumptuous by the senior partners. No question, it was an audacious concept. But, during hours of earnest discussion, both Betts and I had become convinced that to settle for anything less comprehensive might lead to a tragic waste of precious resources and human effort, and to ultimate failure. Then, all past gallant sacrifices in the war would be perceived as having been made in vain: British honour—let alone any glow of victory—would be doomed to lie forever extinguished under the implacable Crimean snows.

So we boldly set down the final tally of our requirements. First, the Civil Engineering Corps' manpower strength—580 men. Then the ships—twenty-three in number, and purchased outright or chartered—which would be needed to get the expedition to Balaklava on time. Each vessel would carry a mixed load of men and materials: in that way no single mishap on an outward voyage would jeopardise the thrust of our overall construction programme.

As well as pay, every category of supplies had been provisionally costed, as Mr. Peto had demanded. The sheer volume of requirements told their own story. They included 1800 tons of GWR rails and fastenings, 6,000 sleepers, 600 loads of timber, 3,000 tons of plant and material, navvies' huts and clothing, stationary engines, wire ropes, cranes, pile drivers, well-sinking gear, wagons, barrows, blocks, chain falls, picks, bars, capstans, sawing machines, forges and carpenters' and smiths' tools.

During the long hours of our labours we had moments of light relief, sometimes occasioned by Mr. Peto and Mr. Brassey themselves who quickly developed the habit of dropping in with ideas and titbits of information, and quietly radiating support for all the world, as Betts remarked to me one morning after they had gone, like parent birds feeding newly-fledged offspring. They certainly made a tall and striking pair, hovering over us as we sat grappling with flying sheets of paper. Their ability to carry extremely complicated calculations in their heads was something I wished to emulate.

The news they brought had been exciting. Several of Mr. Peto's colleagues in the House were now openly discussing the scandal of the Army's position, and had indicated their personal support for his railway scheme, if approved. The Home Secretary had himself privately urged that the proposal be put to the Secretary for War without delay; there was even a strong unofficial hint that an appointment with the Duke of Newcastle might be tentatively pencilled in for Wednesday, 29th November. So far, so good!

Even more heartening were the results of Mr. Brassey's confidential soundings among railway chairmen and engineering suppliers. Unanimously, all had agreed to release vital equipment to us, on demand. On learning that our enterprise would be operating on a non-profit basis, some had even indicated their intention to provide supplies at cost.

Thus spurred, Betts and I brought the last pages of our report to a ringing conclusion. After a final critical re-reading, the foolscap sheets were collated and immediately handed over to a smiling Deacon for fair copying.

'A good job done, I think we could say, Beatty,' Betts reflected, as he stood up, stretching his legs and eyeing the discarded piles of torn paper littering the boardroom table, 'I've enjoyed every minute of it.'

'Better wait for the verdict,' I found myself counselling, with a caution unusual for me. I had no illusion about what was at stake— nothing less than my professional reputation as an engineer.

The next day Mr. Peto and Mr. Brassey would sit in judgement on our plan... afterwards, if that went well, the Duke of Newcastle, and lastly the Prime Minister. Then, DV [God willing], it would be: 'Forward, brave hearts, for the Crimea!' After that, it would be up to me, me alone, to drive the whole project through to its conclusion.

Yet, inside, I felt quietly confident of the outcome. As Betts and I turned out into the street, not even the fog that had been hanging about all day could dampen my spirits. I revelled in a silent walk home—at the first civilised hour since our meetings had started, looking forward to a relaxed evening with Sarah.

Wearing my favourite red wool dress, she looked as young and vital as when we had first met, at a small parish fete in Drumkeen organised by her father. As she sat listening to my story of the day with the firelight flickering across her face, it was hard to realise that she had already borne three children—even more difficult to grasp that within a few months she might be facing another confinement. She would know for certain in a few days. In those few days anything might happen to the Beatty family.

2

A PROMISE AND A HALF

Friday, 1ˢᵗ December

I was up, shaved and dressed by 7 am, too impatient to do any kind of justice to the breakfast Sarah had cooked, and was promptly scolded: 'You've no notion when you'll next be eating, Jim, and it's a horrid morning.' It looked it, too, but when the special messenger arrived with Mr. Peto's note summoning me for an 11 am meeting, I was out of the house like a shot, relieved that the hour of decision had arrived at last.

But as I stepped out on to the pavement of Blomfield Terrace, the Paddington world I knew had vanished: a solid blanket of acrid fog rasped the throat and stung my eyes, making familiar objects blurred and insubstantial. Bulky shapes of drays loomed out of an eerie gloom, darkening by the minute, though it was only just ten o'clock. Even the rumble of iron-hooped wheels seemed strangely muffled.

The contrast of the foggy wilderness of the London streets with the formality of our boardroom meeting at head office was striking— chilling almost. Mr. Peto, with Mr. Brassey on his right, sat at one side of the long table, each with a copy of our plan in front of him. Betts and I were placed opposite them. I felt the pressures we had subjected ourselves to during the past four days rising now to a new level of tension: it was only to be expected. All of us knew the stakes were high. By comparison with the two senior partners—and Betts, too, to a lesser extent—my own individual professional concern paled in significance. Here represented at the table was the largest single contracting company in the country, both men of world-wide acclaim prepared to put their reputation on the line for a scheme I had, in part, helped to devise.

There was no 'feeding of fledglings' in their approach that

morning; but a searching examination of every aspect of our plan which continued in appraising terms for what seemed to me hours. I was only half-aware of the grandfather clock in the corner chiming, then chiming again, as minutes slid by under the intense questioning. Every problem area was identified and put under minute scrutiny. Any possible weaknesses—and omissions, too—were probed by expert questioners determined to eradicate any shortcomings. Towards the end of the morning, my own voice began to sound strange to my ears as I strove to make my points and opinions succinct and positive. I admired Betts for his poise and candour, and especially the occasional dry quip with which he enlivened his comments.

Then the pressure, which seemed to be intensifying as inexorably as the fog that thickened in the street outside, suddenly eased. Mr. Peto turned to his companion with a smile: 'Well, Tom, any further questions?'

'I'm satisfied,' was the quiet reply, and Mr. Brassey laid down the last of our many sheets.

'And so am I,' declared Mr. Peto forcefully. 'Accept our congratulations, gentlemen!'

The effect on the whole room was electrifying. I felt as though an overpowering burden had been lifted from my shoulders. Our scheme and timetable had, with only minor modifications, been approved in its entirety. From now on, the full power and authority of our whole organisation would be united behind it. Overjoyed, I paid but scant attention to the concluding discussion on exactly how the proposal might best be presented to the Duke of Newcastle the following morning. I did take note, though, of Mr. Brassey's final comment. 'Keep it simple, Sam,' he had urged. 'Don't overwhelm him with figures; he gets enough of those from his so-called War Department expert. Stick to the targets we've pledged to meet.'

That next day was sheer drama from start to finish. Mr. Peto's formal meeting with the Duke had been fixed for noon: Betts and I had been requested to wait in an ante-room, in case of possible queries or questions. It was dark and airless, and we had soon wearied of the gloomy military portraits on the bare walls. Another part of my

15

brain was registering the fact that, at that same hour, Dr. John Clarke would be paying his promised call on Sarah at our home to confirm her pregnancy. If her prediction was to be proved correct, we should be welcoming a new Beatty sometime in May of 1855.

I had just changed chairs to avoid the stony glare of one elderly Hussar general when Mr. Peto was shown out of the private office by the Duke himself. His Grace, Mr. Peto told us in high glee, had the plan and strategy in their entirety, and would be recommending it immediately to the Prime Minister for final approval. One way or the other, the matter would be settled on the very next day, Friday, 1st December. One way or the other...

Betts and I were to be at head office, to await the outcome of Mr. Peto's and the Duke's meeting with Lord Aberdeen.

It seemed entirely appropriate that we both should have arrived simultaneously at the bottom of the steps, only a few hundred yards from the scene of Mr. Peto's great building triumph—the new Houses of Parliament, completed by him just seven years earlier.

'Hello, Beatty,' he shouted, cheerfully gesturing through the fog. 'Anyone might think we lived here!' The heavy front door was quickly opened by Deacon who led us straight through to the boardroom. 'Mr. Peto said he might be some time with the Prime Minister, gentlemen. Would you care for coffee—as usual?' he added with a smile.

'We're all right,' said Betts, opening a copy of *The Times* he had brought with him. Deacon paused to make sure the fire was drawing well, and left us.

I looked around the room that we had virtually lived in for the past few days. The only change was that our unused piles of paper had been neatly transferred to side tables, and the revealed dark mahogany of the boardroom table shone with reflected light from the gas lamps along the walls. I walked across to the two tall windows behind Mr. Peto's chair at the head of the table. Through the net curtains the street had a lurid yellow hue. Between the windows hung the only picture in the room. It was a delicate engraving of a small but elegant farmhouse, framed by a modest garden surrounded by trees— Whitmore House, in Surrey, where Mr. Peto's father, William, had once farmed, and where he himself had been born in 1809. I had often studied it while waiting for meetings; its simple charm and reflective atmosphere had captivated me immediately, taking me straight back to my childhood days in the Fermanagh countryside.

Mr. William Peto's eldest son had, I mused, come a long way since that humble beginning. Now only forty-five, Mr. Samuel Morton Peto was nationally known—as a Free Trade member for Norwich for the past nine years, as a leading Baptist, and as an entrepreneur operating in four continents. He had come up the hard way, though: apprenticed at fourteen to his uncle, a local builder, to learn the trade—he could lay his 800 bricks a day along with any skilled man, he said to me once.

Concern for working people and their rights was a ruling passion. In Parliament he had fought successfully to suppress the notorious tommy-shops, which put itinerant navvy gangs at the mercy of unscrupulous sub-contractors; though a teetotaller himself, he would allow any of his men to bring their gallon of beer on to the working of a morning.

This fellow feeling for his employees was reciprocated: on one notable occasion, at the conclusion of a successful railway contract in France, he had been driven—sitting on the front of the engine— through cheering lines of his navvies to the reception dais at the terminus.

This concern for others might well, I had thought, have sprung from the early death of his first wife which had left him with two daughters and a son to bring up. Even after re-marrying he had continued to show interest in my small family: when I had first gone to New Brunswick for the firm, he had called more than once at our London house to enquire after the well-being of Sarah and the girls. Such gestures had put me strongly in mind of my own father's attitude to his patients—'my friends,' as he used to call them. When my mother died at thirty and I was just six years old, the 'Old Doctor' had striven to give us five children a secure home through difficult early years. That care for us had continued unflaggingly, too, through the grim '30s when cholera had swept through our district and my father's self-imposed responsibilities as superintendent of the Enniskillen Cholera Hospital had well-nigh overwhelmed him.

The grandfather clock chimed the half-hour; then, three-quarters. Surely, I thought, wandering distractedly about the room, the Prime Minister's meeting must end soon. Sensing my pent-up frustration, Betts had looked up from his newspaper. 'Maybe, for all his eloquence, the Duke is having his work cut out to drag a decision out of our old and hesitant Prime Minister,' he remarked.

'Won't our "no-profit" stipulation strike a responsive chord in Lord Aberdeen's heart, however dour a Scot he is?'

'He's dour all right, and wily, too. He'll be doubly on his guard against being swept off his feet by another of Newcastle's enthusiasms. The Duke has charm, and a prodigious facility with words; he is also at heart something of a gambler. What he relishes in our plan is the heaven-sent opportunity it presents to get a major operation moving under his wing, without interference from the palsied grasp of his army bureaucrats. When you think about it, Beatty, ours is the first really imaginative idea to be proposed since the start of this disastrous campaign. No, the Duke can hardly believe his luck. We must just pray that his luck holds and that he'll go on giving us his backing—and that he won't get tipped out of office before we start.'

'But first he has to win over the Prime Minister.'

'Between you and me, Beatty, I'm sure Lord Aberdeen has already been persuaded, if not by the Duke then by the latest news.' Betts tapped the paper with his pencil. 'Listen to this—Russell's last dispatch from the Crimea: "There is nothing to eat, no medicine, no clothes, no arrangement—the only thing is abundance of cholera." He wrote that in early November: think what it must be like out there today! Imagine how it will strike a Prime Minister who esteems himself a man of peace. He and Field Marshal Lord Raglan may well have been friends since boyhood, but my guess is that he's itching now to put some backbone into his Commander-in-Chief—anything to get him and his shaky Government out of an untenable situation.'

'You sound confoundedly plausible, Betts,' I exclaimed, 'but, heavens above, they've been talking the *whole* morning! He must have made his mind up by now.'

The grandfather clock struck noon.

'Be realistic, my dear Beatty. To us the matter is straightforward: *we know* the railway can save the army and win the war.'

'Yes; of course—'

'From the Government's point of view there's no unqualified "of course." Consider the course of events: the Cabinet slid into this unwarrantable war in a kind of collective dream—so rumour has it, and Newcastle has admitted as much to his friends. Do you know, Beatty, he tried to get a dispatch approved ordering Raglan to move from Bulgaria to the Crimea early last summer; no one would let him read it! He tried again, after dinner, so it's said, and they just mumbled. So, in desperation, he finally sent it off, hoping piously that poor Raglan would cope. Since then, everything has slipped through their fingers—we lack strategy; army departments dither, and politically the French hold us prisoner!'

'No wonder Lord Aberdeen is weighing up his decision this morning very, very carefully. If he backs our project and it succeeds, he'll be a hero; should it fail, he and his colleagues will go to the wall, with raging condemnation from every vested military interest.'

'Who are you—Devil's Advocate?'

Betts smiled. 'Maybe, maybe not,' he said. 'But I think I can guess what Lord Aberdeen will eventually decide. He will—'

The boardroom door was flung wide open. In came Mr. Peto, his face alight.

'We've won,' he exclaimed, throwing his overcoat and hat on to a chair. 'Sorry to have kept you two so long, but the news is worth any amount of waiting for. We've won the day—totally!'

Betts and I sat silent, digesting every word as Mr. Peto recounted the story of his morning—a morning of surprises, as he observed. The Duke had shown him immediately into the Prime Minister's room at the House. It was then he had had his first surprise: Lord Aberdeen had risen from his desk and advanced to greet him, smiling and with a firm handshake. Never before had he seen the Prime Minister so cordial. He had come to the point at once—that was the second surprise, for directness was not Lord Aberdeen's customary mode of address. He said he had given the proposal much thought since the

Secretary of State for War had first outlined it to him the day before—which he had done with great clarity and conviction. A third surprise, added Mr. Peto, since the Prime Minister was not noted for praise of senior colleagues. Lord Aberdeen had then said plainly: 'I am deeply impressed by the scope of your plan and even more by the terms in which you have expressed it. It does you and your colleagues, sir, great credit. I and my Cabinet are happy to accept your proposal in its entirety, and I want you to know, my dear Peto, that I consider your offer a most handsome, patriotic gesture.' Mr. Peto concluded: 'He shook my hand again, and I came away.'

'Then it's victory,' exclaimed Betts.

'Absolute victory,' replied Mr. Peto. 'We're to have complete control of every aspect—transport, construction, all subsequent running and maintenance.'

Including responsibility for recruiting and managing the workforce, free of Army interference ?' I asked.

'At all stages,' replied Mr. Peto, firmly. 'I made that abundantly clear: manpower is the key factor; that's where your expertise comes in, Beatty. When I told him that you were to be our engineer-in-chief he expressed himself as delighted. The Duke had obviously briefed him on your record, particularly in Nova Scotia last winter.' He then added, smiling: 'You may consider your appointment confirmed at the highest level.'

I could find nothing to say in reply, conscious only of the grave regard of my colleagues, and aware of the weight of responsibility now suddenly laid on me. But, I had to confess, I did not feel dismayed; this, after all, was what I had striven for all my working life—the chance to play a worthy role in a great enterprise, as much for a cause as for personal advantage.

Silently, I vowed to be worthy of this trust placed in me so open-heartedly. It put me vividly in mind of the unspoken feelings that had bound me and my teams together in the Canadian wilderness and in earlier, though smaller, railway projects across England. Differences of scale there might be, but the driving spirit was the same throughout—and *I was to have the picking of the men.*

Still feeling somewhat tongue-tied, I blurted out: 'Why then did your meeting last so long, Mr. Peto?'

Tickled perhaps by the bluntness of my question, Mr. Peto explained how the Prime Minister had insisted on personally going through every one of our supporting papers, checking estimates and searching keenly for discrepancies. But the detail we two had supplied had, in the end, entirely convinced him; he had accepted the conclusions in full.

'There were other reasons why the meeting went on so long,' added Mr. Peto, deliberately. 'I gave Lord Aberdeen two further pledges—on the spur of the moment—and they took a while to spell out.'

'Whatever pledges would those be, Sam?' asked Betts, astonished.

'I promised that we would start the operation this very day and that the first shipload of men and materials would leave England for the Black Sea within a fortnight. That fairly stunned him: he told Newcastle to alert Lord Raglan at once.'

'Well, so be it,' rejoined Betts. 'We had, I agree, discussed such a possibility among ourselves. It's all or nothing, and time is short.'

'That is not quite all that I pledged,' said Mr. Peto, fixing his brother-in-law with a level gaze. 'I promised that as soon as we had unloaded at Balaklava we would have the railway operational in three weeks—and would lay seven miles of track in seven weeks.'

'Now that I call a promise and a half, Sam!' exclaimed Betts. 'We had no survey: all Beatty and I had to work on were a few sketchy, out-of-date maps and some rough pencil drawings of the lie of the land made by a cavalry general.'

'Quite so—but it didn't stop you forecasting a spanking rate of progress, Edward. I have every faith in your figures and in Beatty's drive. He can do it: I'm sure of that.' Turning to me, he asked: 'Can't you, Beatty?'

'I'll do my best, but—'

'Your best, that's all I ask. The line must go through, and exactly to the schedule you set out—night and day working—your precise words, remember? My old family motto is *Press forward*. It's simple

21

and unrelenting, but it works,' he added with a smile.

He had told Mr. Brassey the news as soon as he had left Lord Aberdeen, and he was expecting him in a few minutes: he would be a tower of strength. Meanwhile, our very best people were to be involved at once; the Crimean enterprise had to take precedence over all other company operations.

When Mr. Brassey was announced by Deacon, the boardroom table was once again awash with paper—plant lists, itemised stores, staff names, draft telegrams to ship-owners and brokers—and the three of us were deep in discussion. He signalled us to continue, and took a chair beside Betts. From his quiet manner it was difficult to realise that here was a man who, in his own right, was by far the biggest single railway contractor in the world.

In the intervals of making notes I was able to study him close at hand for the first time. Previously, all I had seen of him over the years were distant glimpses when he was visiting scattered contracts. His head was striking, with a broad forehead, aquiline nose and surprisingly widely-spaced grey eyes. A firm chin framed a full-lipped mouth that held a hint of wry humour at the corners. Mr. Brassey came from an old Cheshire land-owning family and had long been a friend of Mr. George Stephenson. He was, interestingly, in his spare time, a notable collector of porcelain. Tall and spare, his quiet presence effortlessly dominated our little group.

I knew from several of his senior managers who were friends of mine in what esteem he was held as an employer. They often told me of the care he took in selecting his agents; how he was prepared to listen to their problems; would make his mind up quickly—and then back them to the hilt. One of his staff veterans once confided: 'I found myself running Mr. Brassey's business as though it were my own.'

'One other thing came out of this morning's meeting, Tom,' said Mr. Peto, looking up at his friend. 'I was instructed—at the highest level—not to omit anything essential on grounds of cost: all budgets would be fully met. What do you think of that, eh?'

'If I were a cynic I'd say it sounded like any politician in desperate straits,' replied Mr. Brassey, with a chuckle. 'However, you're highly practised at handling this breed, Sam; that's your department. The same goes for you, Edward, as far as supplies and transport are concerned. It strikes me that it's Beatty here who, of all of us, has by far the really tough job—putting together a rock-solid workforce from scratch, ready to be shipped off for action in a fortnight.'

Giving me a shrewd but kindly glance, he asked: 'How are you going to set about it?'

'There'll only be a small staff of officers,' I replied, 'and I'm counting on getting several who've worked with me before—men like Donald Campbell, as chief surveyor. I've thrown out a few broad hints already, but of course I couldn't make definite offers until today. I doubt if I'll get many refusals.' Mr. Brassey laughed.

'As for navvies and craftsmen, I shall start recruiting tomorrow morning. We've taken a temporary office at 41 Waterloo Road, next door to the York Hotel: I've found it an excellent hunting ground in the past.'

'And the rent's only a guinea a day,' interjected Betts. 'No one can say we're squandering Government funds.'

'I aim to get the job completed by next Monday,' I said. 'It's all the timetable will allow. I hope a notice like this in the window will fetch 'em in smartly.' I unrolled the poster I'd roughed out on the parlour table that morning, and held it up. The thick letters and strong black border stood out boldly from the white paper:

WANTED

SKILLED MEN

for

CIVIL ENGINEERING CORPS

IN THE CRIMEA

PETO, BRASSEY AND BETTS

Apply within

'Capital! exclaimed Mr. Brassey. 'Short and to the point. It must go up at once.'

'I'll get Deacon to see to it,' said Betts briskly, and stretching across the table, took it from my hand and left the boardroom.

'Action stations! That's what I like to see,' said Mr. Brassey, rising. 'I'll be away, too, Sam; I want to nobble Robert Stephenson over the costings. Don't stir, please. I'll see myself out.'

* * * * * * *

There was no doubting the depth of Mr. Peto's commitment to the venture. 'We must not, dare not, fail,' he repeated, as he shook hands with us at the front door. Forgotten were all personal concerns—his business, his seat in the Commons that he would now, according to the rules, be compelled to vacate. He, along with Betts and me, was totally fired by the vision of this railway that would transform the war and save the lives of thousands. A dream it might be, but very real to the three of us at that moment, carried along as on some mighty flood...

Sarah, too, I reflected, as I waited on the foggy pavement for a hansom cab back to our home, would also be experiencing a similar wave of expectation. But though this railway might spell fulfilment for me, for my sweet Sal it only heralded months, perhaps years, of anxiety and loneliness. Yet, I thought, we were still young: Sarah was a woman of rare faith and fortitude. Separation, as we had both had to acknowledge, was part of the price we had to pay for my chosen way of life.

All philosophical musings vanished abruptly as she opened the door and I saw her eyes: they were dancing with delight. I knew, without asking, the cause of her joy—she was expecting our baby! I kissed her sweet mouth and folded her in my arms.

3

NO SHRINKING VIOLETS

Saturday, 2nd December

Approaching our temporary office in the Waterloo Road at six o'clock next morning was like entering another world. I was heartened to see lights already on inside; and a great press of men out in the street, laughing, smoking, wrestling among themselves and cursing the fog.

Henry Burke, Sarah's young brother, all eagerness at the prospect of a foreign assignment as one of my assistant surveyors, had set off at a run from my home half an hour before me to pick up Bob Shaw on the way, and square up the rooms for the day's work ahead. I had good hopes of young Shaw, one of our four timekeepers; he was cool and level-headed, but full of spirit.

My arrival was greeted with a cheer from the crowd milling around on the pavement, gesticulating at our poster in the window.

'When's opening time, sir?' one called out in unmistakable Irish brogue.

'Seven sharp.'

'Sure we're all waiting, Mr. Beatty.' I warmed to the cheerful tone, and walked through the men into the front office.

Standing by Henry's newly-lit fire were the three men I had urgently summoned—Donald Campbell, John Kellock and Edgar Swan—my closest associates. I shook their hands warmly and was very glad to feel an equally firm pressure in return from each.

'We saw your poster s-soon as we got here,' said Campbell, grinning widely and stammering as he always did when excited. The others were smiling, too. Kellock was thin and highly-strung, Swan short and stocky, but Campbell was a bear of a man, slow-moving but with immense reserves of strength and tenacity. He seemed twice the size of the others.

I walked towards one of the two inner offices where coal fires were already burning. 'Come in here,' I said, 'I've a lot to tell you.' They followed me in, taking off their coats and sitting down eagerly opposite me round a scratched old desk.

'I expect you guessed the other day why I was sounding you out,' I said. 'But I couldn't do more than hint then. Now I can tell you: our Crimean railway project is in the open with a vengeance! The Prime Minister approved it yesterday and PB&B are to carry it out, starting immediately. Mr. Peto has promised Lord Aberdeen that the first shipload of men and materials will leave for Balaklava within a fortnight.'

Campbell gave a long whistle. 'By 15th December?' he asked . I nodded.

'I've been appointed engineer-in-chief, so now I'm able to make each of you a firm offer—as assistant engineers. The contract's for at least six months, possibly a year. Salary: five hundred pounds.' I paused and looked straight at the intent faces of my colleagues. 'What do you say?'

Immediate acceptance was their response—spontaneous and wholehearted.

'We'll talk about individual responsibilities later,' I went on. 'Today our job is to pick the men—we want the finest railway workforce ever raised.'

'How long have we got?'

'Just two days—today and Monday: time's against us, I'm afraid.'

'How many men are we talking about?' asked Edgar Swan.

'I want five hundred and fifty, top-rate. There are bound to be some drop-outs.'

'Here's the shopping list I drew up last night: have a look at it.' There was silence in the small office as I handed each of them a sheet of paper.

While they were reading, I was listening to the rising hubbub from the street—an encouraging sound. But I could hear some ugly

26

shouts as well, and cursed the York Hotel for opening up its bars so quickly. It wouldn't make our task any easier. It was only 6.35 am! But at least, word of our call for men had spread like wildfire round the neighbourhood. There would be pandemonium out there when we opened the outer door for business.

We were in for a noisy day, that was certain. These were no shrinking violets, but navvies, sometimes violent, but always bursting with energy, proud of their skills and endurance, sullen if crossed though equally quick to respond to praise, their only relaxation being Saturday night drinking bouts in cramped shanties far away from home. They had come from all parts but belonged nowhere: survivors of Irish potato famines, redundant Gloucestershire weavers, radicals from northern industrial slums, labourers whose strength and determination alone had steered them past a poorhouse existence. Men who, in their butty gangs, would tear into a hill for three shillings a day, tunnel through a mountain with water above their boots, disdainful of any threat of roof-fall or shattered limb. Men, whose strange custom was to work their long shifts in silence, with only the Welsh among them punctuating rare moments of rest with an old hymn tune.

This was our raw material, daunting to deal with at the best of times. Now what was demanded was nothing less than an elite force: I felt we could produce it. With growing confidence I consulted my list, and read out:

> 350 navvies, platelayers and miners
> 20 gangers
> 20 rough masons or bricklayers
> 100 carpenters and 3 foremen
> 30 well sinkers
> 28 blacksmiths and 2 foremen
> 12 engine-drivers and fitters

I looked across at my companions. 'Well, that's the tally. I want half that number today, and the rest on Monday. There'll be a fresh lot then as word gets about on Sunday. We'll see the men two at a time.

27

Donald, you and I can use this office. Kellock, will you and Swan set up shop next door?'

'What are the men's terms?' Campbell asked. 'They may only be interested in getting a place, but their w-wives will want to know.'

'A good point—never forget the women,' I exclaimed. 'Daily pay will be from five shillings to eight shillings, according to a man's trade, plus clothing and Commissariat rations. Men to supply their own tools. Free passage to the Crimea and back. All men to be of good character and personally known to one or other of us four, wherever possible. All recruits to sign an agreement acknowledging my authority: I've had a thousand copies printed. There are also forms here for allocating regular sums from their pay to families. That goes for staff, too. I intend making over all my salary and living off official rations.'

'Please God we weed out all wrong 'uns!' exclaimed Kellock, gesturing with his thumb at the steadily-rising racket in the street, a roar of talk, scuffling and laughter punctuated by loud impatient thumps on the street door.

His remark gave me my first chuckle of the morning: 'We'll be lucky to get ten per cent of angels, John, but I'd hope not to be ordering too many floggings. Believe me, anyone not making the grade—men or staff—will be on the first boat for England.'

I called in our two assistants from the front office, Bob Shaw and Henry, my young brother-in-law, a tall, eager lad, who so far had never been further from his County Fermanagh home than the one journey to our home in London. I wondered again whether I had been right in attaching him to our perilous undertaking, but he had finished his training as a surveyor, and his pleadings had won my initially reluctant consent.

'We're ready to start now,' I told them. 'Only let a dozen into the outer room at a time: make sure the rest don't rush you. Then send one at a time into each of the offices.'

'Right, Mr. Beatty,' replied Shaw. 'I've recognised several from our old gangs through the window—eight from Nova Scotia days and a whole crowd from the Tilbury line. They're making a fair old stir out there. You'd think they were off on a randy!'

'Worried the war'll be over before they get to the Crimea,' added Henry. 'I've just heard one of them threatening to get at "them Roosians" with a pickaxe or his bare hands.'

'Remind them they're a *civil* engineering corps, not soldiers,' I replied curtly. 'Let's start.'

Every man we saw was indeed desperate for a place, not for money or thrills, but just to help our troops—and, no doubt, to give The Bear [Russia] a bloody nose if a chance arose.

What I wanted was a solid nucleus of seasoned men—gangers and navvies and essential craftsmen—and we were fortunate in what we found. Many skilled men had been employed on our Victoria Dock scheme; others had been for years on Mr. Peto's Houses of Parliament contracts.

I had privately decided to aim for a mix of qualities—in gangers, experience and leadership; in navvies, youth and strength. Yet, I did finally select a fair number of older men. Such a policy had paid off handsomely on previous tough contracts, where commitment and the will to succeed were as much a matter of hard-won self belief as of brawn.

Interviewing went on non-stop at a hectic pace; there was barely time for more than a snatched beer and a hurried sandwich brought in by Henry from the York, and as darkness fell the piles of new recruits' papers grew high on our desks. When we finally emerged, exhausted, into the foggy night we were literally mobbed again. The whole street was blocked from side to side with agitated men who set up a great shout, brandishing their shovels aloft, as though demanding to be taken on.

'We start again Monday morning at seven,' I shouted, and was greeted with a rising volume of cheers and calls. I turned to my weary team: 'Good night; thank you; well done. I'll see you, too, on Monday—at six.' They nodded. 'Henry, tell Sarah I've gone to report progress to Mr. Betts, and I'll be home for supper as soon as we've finished the paperwork.'

Walking slowly along the river and over Westminster Bridge to the office I reviewed the efforts of the day. All told, we had taken on nearly 300 men. Without question we should reach our target of 550 on Monday. Then only my own task of selecting the staff—timekeepers, storekeepers, draughtsmen, as well as surgeons, nurses, scripture readers, a horsemaster—and, for good measure, a barber, would remain! Personal recommendations and private canvassing would, I felt sure, see the mission accomplished swiftly, aided by the challenge and novelty of the enterprise, and the fact that the war had halted a number of construction projects: good staff were, thank God, more readily available.

Betts heard my tale out, and nodded quiet approval at our progress. His day had started nearly as early as mine, he told me, but his eyes still had a sparkle and his tone was confident. He had drawn up a master-list of tasks. The many red ticks against individual items on the four foolscap sheets bore testimony to the speed and tenacity with which he had acted.

Urgent letters and telegrams for substantial orders had left his desk throughout that long day, addressed to engineering firms, railway companies and ship-owners. Interspersed with the almost non-stop dictation to the clerks had been hurriedly-arranged interviews with London suppliers and agents.

'So far, so good,' he murmured; then, catching my eye, added with a grin: 'The fact that the Government is guaranteeing prompt payment for all materials (after audit) has encouraged a tremendous response from all of them.'

'That's good,' I exclaimed.

'And it's the shipping people who have surprised me most,' Betts continued. 'They can sometimes be irritatingly slow, but, do you know, I've already been promised all the vessels we'll need for the first sailing dates. I bought our first ship today: *Wildfire*—rather an auspicious name, don't you think? She's 457 tons, and a very fast clipper; she'll be fitted out, ready for us to leave Birkenhead, fully laden, on 15th December. In fact,' he added with satisfaction, 'all the ships I'm getting are the most up-to-date available. The 800-ton screw-steamer *Hesperus* will be ready by the end of the month, and the rest in January.'

I looked down the list he held out to me: five more screw steamers—*Lady Alice Lampton* (511 tons), *Great Northern* (578 tons), *Baron von Humboldt* (420 tons), *Earl of Durham* (554 tons) and *Prince of Wales* (627 tons). Lastly, a 694-ton paddle steamer, *Levant* and the clipper *Mohawk*, of 850 tons.

'This is, I calculate, about one-third of the fleet we will eventually need,' said Betts. 'We reckoned twenty-three ships in all would be enough to handle the job, with shiploads split into self-contained units, each carrying fifty to eighty men under an assistant engineer and two gangers; plus surgeon and clerk storekeeper. All construction material to be similarly divided, along with tarpaulin sheets, fodder, coal, coke and firewood, tents, sectioned huts, loose boards and scantlings. And for each ten men, a portable cooking stove. How's that?!'

'Excellent,' I exclaimed. 'You're not forgetting the men's tobacco?'

'How could I forget,' laughed Betts. 'You're as bad as any of them, with your infernal cigars. No, two pounds per man it stands at.'

'Now, as to clothing—' I began. Betts broke in: 'They follow your scales exactly, though I still think they're a trifle on the over-protective side.'

He passed another paper across. 'We both know about winters: remember New Brunswick in '52?'

Betts made no reply. I studied the details with satisfaction. Nothing could contrast more strikingly with what the wretched soldiers had to put up with—clothed in rags and often with no boots. Our corps could face any climate with the kit we were issuing. Each man would have his own bed, pillow, blankets and rug. Clothes included striped cotton shirts, red flannel shirts, moleskin trousers and waistcoat, padded pea-jacket lined with flannel, topped off with multi-coloured cravat and red bobble-hat—the navvy's trademark. Completing this kit-for-all-weathers were drawers, worsted stockings, ankle jack laced boots, mittens, high boots for mud, waterproofs and sou'westers.

'I'd feel like a king in that lot,' I remarked, 'but I have a notion every item will be needed by the time we're through. The staff and I will see to our own gear,' I added, 'and I'll consult with our chief surgeon over medical supplies when I've found the right man.'

'Our enterprise has certainly caught the attention of the Press,' remarked Betts, turning over his notes. 'I've had one young man from the *Illustrated London News* camping out here in the office most of the day. He's kept plaguing me to allow him to copy stuff off my sheets for his next issue. In the end I agreed; it wasn't strictly confidential—just lists of material and plant already secured, but I must admit it gave quite a gratifying impression of the size of the operation. At least it should encourage our suppliers.

'And,' he continued, 'I've got a solution to the problem of the stationary engines for working the incline. I couldn't get new ones from any manufacturer, but Tom Brassey reminded me this morning of the five we'd recently installed at the Victoria Docks. He volunteered to put personal pressure on the directors for a temporary loan of some of them. Result—we're getting three of their brand-new engines next week!'

'Finishing contracts on schedule always pays dividends,' I remarked.

'You're right there, Beatty. It's a tactic that has its own special appeal. I've had quite a day of visitors—I daresay you could say the same! Who should drop by unexpectedly but our staunch old friend, Robert Stephenson. He's desperately keen for this railway to succeed; said he would volunteer for the Crimea himself to help things forward—if only, said he, he were beyond the range of the artillery!'

The muffled rattle of carriage wheels was still echoing along Great George Street as I rose to leave. 'A long day, but a good one,' I said. 'The same'll go for Monday, that's for sure. Goodnight.'

'I've got a couple more interviews yet: scripture readers, highly recommended by one of Mr. Peto's Baptist friends.' Before I had closed the boardroom door, Betts, still smiling, had picked up his pen and was starting yet another letter to a supplier.

I hailed a hansom and went home in style, reflecting on the day's encounters. So many faces—foremost among them those of my colleagues, chosen companions for the venture; I warmed at the memory of their enthusiasm. I swear, that, for two pins, Donald Campbell would have given us all one of his bear-hugs! There were, naturally enough, some new faces among the navvies, anxious to impress; but many more, too, of those known and tested over the years. One such—and most welcome—was old Tom Grace, one of my gangers on two successive contracts, once a farm labourer at Melbury in Dorset, slow of speech but with a mind keen as a scythe.

He had pushed his way in early on, and plumped himself firmly down opposite Campbell and me, determined to secure his place. He had caught my mood of optimism, and sensed instinctively one of its sources. 'It's all down to that Mr. Brassey, i'n't it, sir,' he exclaimed, jabbing his old worn pipe stem at me, in emphasis. 'Along wi' Mr. Peto, 'e's our great man, an' this corps 'ere'll prove a grand show. I tell 'ee, if Mr. Brassey 'ad been a parson 'e'd 'ave been a bishop; an' if 'e'd been a prize-fighter 'e'd 'ave won the Belt! An' 'im so quiet always in 'is ways.'

* * * * * * *

'Darling Sal,' I said, kissing her on the doorstep, I've kept you late for supper, but Henry will have told you about our day. Hundreds of men clamouring—'

'For goodness sake, Jim, don't stand there talking, come in and let me shut the door—it's a dreadful night.' She took off my coat and pushed me briskly into the parlour, where a great fire was glowing. I was shivering, though its warmth soon enveloped me. Oddly, the shivering continued, but I recognised this as a personal idiosyncrasy of old—the shivers of excitement experienced since boyhood at moments of exhilaration; such as when as a thirteen-year-old successfully construing a Latin text in my father's study at Enniskillen; later, having earned the approbation of my engineering pupil-master, Mr. Woodhouse, being offered my first salaried post under him on the Midland Counties Railway; and, later still, my courtship of Sarah Jane Burke, with a warm welcome as a son-in-law into a rector's family in County Fermanagh.

'Stop your day-dreaming, Jim, and come and have your supper.' With smiling insistence Sarah pushed me to my chair. One glance at the table, with its steaming soup tureen, sliced meats, potatoes in jackets, cheese and a small decanter of red wine, reminded me just how hungry I was; I tucked in as though I hadn't eaten for days.

We were late getting to bed: I found myself reflecting again on the quality of the men we had so far selected. Would they measure up to the job, however challenging it became? God alone, I thought, knew the answer to that. We might have a more precise idea when we had carried out our second trawl on Monday. Tomorrow would be yet another Sunday at my desk in the small study, considering the men and the final candidates for the staff. Oh, for another two or three of Campbell's calibre! A brilliant surveyor and confirmed bachelor, who had volunteered to come with me to see my first-born son, Wallace, then one month old on that momentous Christmas Day in our tiny rented house on the Halifax waterfront. Normally taciturn, on that occasion he had been so excited he could only stammer his congratulations to Sarah, then make a blushing retreat into admiring silence.

* * * * * * *

Sunday brought a calmer tempo. With breakfast over, Sarah and I quietly talked over the impact this new venture would have on her and the children.

'I didn't marry a stay-at-home, Jim,' she said, smiling. She was absolutely fearless. 'I knew from the start you intended to conquer the world! While both our families have put down good Irish roots—with your sister Lizzie and my brother Michael married, and settled near the parents—you and I came away. Now we've Fanny and Susy, both born here, and our Canadian baby son. When I think about it, those few months in that old clapboard house in Halifax with the two little girls and the arrival of Wallace, were the happiest in my life. Never mind the draughts and the freezing weather, I was sharing a new view of the world with you, my sweetheart, and I'll not forget that time, however grand we may become. So, don't worry about me and the children; God will take care of all of us, and I promise I'll run our affairs well while you're away.'

'You always have done,' I said, with admiration. 'And don't

worry about me; remember, I'll have young Henry there to keep me in order.'

'A *most* steadying influence I'm sure,' said Sarah with a laugh.

'Young Henry is going to work harder than ever before in his life; that's the kind of steadying he'll get! When he gets back, you won't even recognise your young brother.'

* * * * * * *

For the rest of that foggy Sunday I sat in my study, checking over every detail of the new recruits. Out of the 170-odd that Campbell and I had chosen I put question marks against a dozen or so, for further discussion on Monday. He, I felt sure, would have some queries, maybe the same names; so too, probably, would Kellock and Swan. On balance, though, I was for leaving the list largely intact; judgments made in hot blood were likely to prove just as reliable indicators of potential worth as any amount of cold examination later.

I was quietly confident of being able to handle those men, but, when it came to dealing with the military whom I would have to persuade to my way of thinking, that posed a different problem. How should my tactics be with them? My father's maxim came to mind: 'Be strong, straight and steadfast at all times.'

I had done my best to follow this doctrine from the first moment when, as a fifteen-year-old engineer-pupil, I had been pitched head-long into the roar and drama of railway life on the half-built Midland Counties line, where the days ahead seemed endless, nothing but tramping of the rail-bed in all weathers. Later, I had caught a glimpse of another side to this savage activity—the arrival at the works office of such towering figures as Mr. George Stephenson and Mr. Vignoles to discuss progress; also an occasional fleeting inspection by directors of the company that was financing the project. I couldn't say that I had cared much for those money men, but at that stage of my career they were none of my concern, just possible problems the future might bring. I hoped that maxim would hold good in those spheres, too.

Our new civil engineering corps, I was beginning to see, must develop its own inner strength and resolve; it would have to be as wholehearted, as steadfast as any regiment of the line. And it would have our own unique weapon for victory—speed!

Sarah opened the study door. 'Not day-dreaming this time,' I said hastily. 'Strictly feet-on-the-ground stuff!'

'You wouldn't know the difference,' she replied, serenely, 'it's the girls' bath-time now; they're waiting for their Papa.'

I followed her upstairs to the bathroom. The chicks' galvanised tub was full: two water-logged wooden figures of the Duke of Wellington minus most of his bright paint were bobbing about between our little girls. Fanny could just sit up safely, but was still painfully tiny, though already four years old. It was as well that Eliza Bernard had firm hold of little red-headed Susy, for she had been within a whisker of swallowing an enthusiastic, if ill-judged, mouthful of bathwater.

I was looking forward to the day when Wallace would be joining the rout. But this was no time for dreaming: this was the moment for action. I took off my jacket, rolled up my sleeves, and, seizing a Wellington in each hand, sent waves rippling towards the girls...

Bath-time was a happy, noisy and very wet affair.

4

THE BEST PASSPORT

Monday, 4th December

The scene in fog-bound Waterloo Road on the Monday morning was an uncanny replica of the previous Saturday, except for the demeanour of the men who were milling around on the pavement and half-way across the road outside the office, and whose shouts reached me as I crossed the bridge. This time there was an air of desperation about them, an ugly determination not to give ground to any mate.

An icy drizzle added a raw discomfort.

As I reached the door, glad to see the gas lamps already lit inside, more men came hurrying up the street to join the throng. Barring my way was the unexpected figure of Tom Grace.

'You, Tom?' I exclaimed. 'Come to resign before you've even started?'

''Deed no, sir. I spent yesterday rowsting out some o' me ol' gang from the Southampton-Dorchester works: I've a baker's dozen for 'ee.'

'Well done! Bring them in as soon as we start.'

Donald Campbell, Kellock and Swan were already at the desks, mopping faces that shone wetly in the flare of the lamps. They looked determined but cheerful, chatting together like old friends. Henry and Bob Shaw had lit the fires and set out our papers.

'Let's settle queries before we begin,' I said. 'Anyone had second thoughts? How about non-starters? I've fifteen in my batch.'

'About the same for me,' said Campbell. 'Probably the same names, I sh-shouldn't wonder.'

'How about you, Kellock?'

'Twelve's my total, Mr. Beatty,' said John staring at his sheets. 'Real villains some of them; I wonder how they slipped past me.'

'Swan?'

'Nine doubtfuls, I'm afraid.'

'Strike 'em all off the strength, then. We must aim for certain-
ties—or strong hunches—wherever possible. Everything is riding on
the backs of those we take, us included. Let's keep our wits about us
today.'

I called out to Henry: 'Tom Grace told me just now he's ferreted
out some of the old Dorset line men. Let's make sure of them quickly
before that mob raises a riot.'

'Half are trying to get in to us; the other half are queuing for the
York,' remarked Donald, with a grin.

'We're still short of ten seasoned gangers, by my reckoning,' I
said.

'And platelayers and well-sinkers,' added Kellock.

'Blacksmiths, too,' said Swan. 'And talking of horses, who do
you think I ran into yesterday? Old John Parker. He was our
horsemaster on the Victoria Docks contract. A bit long in the tooth
now, but he reckons he's fit for a final trip abroad before he hangs up
his harness.'

'Forty-eight's no age,' said Donald, who, at thirty-seven, prided
himself on his youthfulness. 'But Mrs. John won't let him out of her
sight till he's signed-over his allotment money.' We all smiled,
knowing Mrs. John of old, a salty character, but with the grip of a
bulldog on her husband.

'Amazing how keen the men are to hand over pay,' Donald went
on. He, I knew, was giving all his salary to his widowed mother.

'Not surprising at all,' remarked Swan. 'It's a safeguard, don't
you see? There'll be no pension for any of us if things go wrong.'

'Nothing's going to go wrong,' I said, sharply, 'so long as
everyone buckles down. Remember, we want our full tally today, plus
reserves. Open the front door, Henry!'

In tumbled Tom Grace, his lads hot on his heels—Doddy
Williams, Dick Payling, Andy Warner, 'Fishy' Haddock and the
rest—in the wildest of spirits, looking just the same as when I'd last
seen them three years before.

I heard 'Fishy' cheekily asking Shaw: 'Do I get a rifle, sir?'

'Not you, laddie. Are you sure you're to be trusted with a shovel?' A burst of laughter greeted this sally, and the remark was passed down the lines of men—fiercely jostling each other to get to the door as though competing for front-row places at the music-hall.

Smoke from the men's clay pipes quickly dimmed the light in the offices; the continuous tread of their boots on the wooden floors sounded like thunder. Still, the recruiting went steadily ahead; completed papers piled up on our desks again, as hour followed hour. Half the men I'd ever taken on over the years seemed to be in that anxious, never-ending line. The Black Sea must somehow have sounded as magical to them as the Garden of Eden! And it wasn't only the dread of not being taken on that made them so keen.

Four men I saw told me they had been working in a gang under 'Black Jack' Kemp on a Peak District contract that had come to grief after years of heart-breaking work. I wasn't surprised: rumour had it that the project had had disaster written on it from the start. But they wanted to come in as a gang and hinted that Kemp himself was interested in coming, too. That interested me: I needed another good ganger, and he had a reputation for reliability, despite being heavy-handed in his methods. Impulsively, I decided to take him on—and his gang with him. It was a mistake I was to pay for later.

Darkness was falling as we came to the end. After a last check, I called out to Henry and Shaw:

'That's it: bolt the door. Put this notice in the window.'

NO

MORE

MEN

WANTED

Immediately, angry shouts broke out from those nearest the door. Heavy boots thudded against it, and the office window was shattered by a flung stone. There was despair as well as anger in the voices, and the noise rolled round the street for several minutes. But the demonstration died away. Eventually, the men dispersed, some slipping into the York to drown their sorrows or to cadge a drink from mates who had been taken on.

In the suddenly quiet office, we relaxed with a quick bite of bread and cheese and some beer. 'I'm pleased with today's work,' I said. 'It's an even better bunch than Saturday's. Tom Grace's lads were a real bonus, and we also pulled in some from the old Norwich-Lowestoft contract: I hadn't set eyes on them for eight years.'

Swan said: 'I was tackled by one of our New Brunswick gangers, Enoch Hill—you remember him, Mr. Beatty—the Welshman who always sang a line of a hymn before felling a tree?'

'Indeed, and however hard it was snowing, and before breakfast, look you,' I said with a chuckle. 'He'd have been glad of this cheese then, a darned sight better than all that abominable salt pork!'

While the others smoked their pipes and talked among themselves, I lit a cigar and went through the papers again: the day's total had been 310. I could afford ten per cent for later rejections and last-minute drop-outs. Considering the time pressure on us, this was an acceptable working figure. I had my 550 picked men!

I called Henry and Shaw in from the front office. 'We've got our tally; the next step is to break the number down by trades and shiploads. Kellock and Swan, I need your help on that right away; we've a lot of planning to do to get the first two vessels away on time. Listen carefully: Shaw, I want you to take on *Wildfire*; she'll be sailing from Birkenhead on 15th December.' Shaw gasped. It was the first he'd heard of it, but he grinned, and nodded cheerfully. I had felt this was the best way to break it to him; he was inclined to get anxious if he had too much time to think ahead; once on the job he was imperturbable.

'Kellock, I'm putting you in charge of *Hesperus*, which will leave from London at the end of the month.

'Donald, you'll head up the advance party for the all-important survey. You must be on your way within a week—overland to Marseilles, then the fastest transit to Constantinople and Balaklava. The office will fix the passages.'

'Good, good, Jim,' he said with relish.

'Pick the best for your team: Jack Wright should be a solid Number Two. I need the quickest survey you've ever done, Donald.

We must all pray that the terrain isn't totally unworkable.'

'Mr. Betts' friend, General Evans, didn't sound too happy about it!' said Donald. 'Was he as blunt as you said?'

'He was incandescent!'

'I never could stand a mealy-mouthed man,' observed Donald, with a grin.

'There's nothing polished about de Lacy Evans; he's a cavalry general of the old school, and he's backing us because I've managed to convince him that this railway is the only thing that can save his precious Second Division. As soon as he's fit, he'll be off to the front again.'

Henry broke in: 'While I was locking the front door just now, a man handed me this letter for you, Jim: said he was a surgeon.' I put the envelope in my pocket to read later.

'When do you expect *Wildfire* to reach Balaklava, Mr. Beatty?' asked Bob Shaw.

'By the end of January, all being well,' I replied. 'But I'll be out there before you, and Campbell will have done his survey. Then we'll start to keep Mr. Peto's promise to build seven miles of track in seven weeks!'

I was half expecting trouble when we finally left the office. All bars in the York were jam-packed, and sullen groups of men were lingering on the pavement. Many were drunk and there was a hard core of individuals, maddened at being denied a place and plainly bent on mischief. We made for the bridge, but several tried to catch us up. I quickened my pace, and my colleagues closed in behind me. 'We've got our numbers—sorry, but that's it!' I shouted over my shoulder. A determined few began to run alongside, hurling abuse and throwing random punches. One struck out and sent me sprawling, but Donald dragged me to my feet, and we walked doggedly on. Some of the mob fell back, jeering and throwing stones: Shaw was hit on the head; but by this time we were nearing the crown of the bridge and our attackers had had enough, had run out of steam. Our pace didn't slacken until they were out of earshot.

* * * * * * *

A partners' conference had been in progress for some time when I reached our Westminster office that night. Betts was at the head of the boardroom table, flanked by Mr. Brassey and Mr. Peto. My news of the final workforce totals was greeted with satisfaction.

'Gentlemen, please let me continue,' said Betts, in his usual precise tone. 'To save time and expense I'm buying ships for our armada at ports as near as possible to the works that are making the plant and materials. This should speed up loading considerably. *Wildfire*, for instance, which I got for £4,500 from Tonge, Curry of Liverpool, is now having her between-decks fitted up as cabins with berths for the men. Mr. Scott, our manager of the North of Europe Navigation Company, is superintending this work. We're getting a loan of their ships, too.

'I really can't praise our suppliers highly enough,' Betts went on. 'Take *Hesperus*, the second ship to leave. She is due out from Blackwall Dock at the end of this month, and is now being completed in one of Mitchell's yards at Walker-on-Tyne. At the same time, another of their yards is manufacturing an order of GWR pattern rails for us, and these will be loaded into the hold, warm from the furnace!'

Betts looked delightedly round at us all. 'However, we still have some way to go on the materials side: the sleepers aren't yet cut, and the bulk of the rails have still to be rolled. But, I'm assured, they'll be ready on time. Thanks to Mr. Brassey's persuasion, we've secured three vital stationary engines. Perhaps, Tom, at this stage, you'd like to add a word on the costings side.'

'Robert Stephenson gave me several valuable hours this morning, and we went over my rough figures together,' said Mr. Brassey. 'Cost of plant we estimated at £45,000; freightage at £55,000. Audited bills will be submitted to the Duke of Newcastle next week. The later accounts, in January, look to be around £80,000 for purchase and charter of vessels, £14,000 for medical and nursing staff, and £5,000 for horses, drivers and provender.'

'The Duke sent one of his aides round here this morning,' interjected Betts. 'I suppose to see how we were getting on: he seemed very impressed by the time he left. I sent him off with the news that another couple of firms were putting their men on night shift to speed things up.'

'That's just the kind of support we need,' exclaimed Mr. Peto. 'And yours is a great effort, Beatty: five hundred and fifty men in two days is some going. Are you happy about the quality?'

'That's difficult to estimate till I've seen them on the job. The gangers are first-rate. If the staff are as good, we shall have a Corps out there worthy of the name.'

'Steady, Beatty,' Betts called out. 'Don't overplay your hand.'

Touché, I thought, a trifle conscience-stricken. It was one of my old failings to think all my geese were swans. Sometimes, though, it worked out; it was always worth the gamble, I felt. 'I'm putting Bob Shaw, one of our four timekeepers, in charge of *Wildfire*. He's reliable, and won't stand nonsense from anybody. I plan to travel up myself to Birkenhead with his party, to see the clipper safely off on the 15th.'

'The men's kits are already being got together,' said Betts, 'and, Beatty, do be sure that you and the other officers take adequate personal gear with you. Every one keeps telling me the same thing: what you don't take with you, you'll not find in Balaklava. I suggest the men sign for their kits just as they go on board, by the way.'

'A sensible precaution,' said Mr. Peto. 'All allotment papers, too, should be signed before the men get on the train north.'

'They do understand there's no question of a pension,' said Mr. Brassey. 'It's not in our remit, you know.'

'The conditions are all spelled out in the agreement everyone has signed,' I replied. 'Each man has his copy. Their only grouse is that they're not going to be allowed a crack at the enemy.'

'You could do with an agreement yourself, Beatty, to help crack the military crust,' remarked Mr. Peto. 'I said as much to Lord Aberdeen the other morning, but I'm not sure how much he took in. However, the Duke got the point at once. Lord Stratford, our ambassador in Constantinople is, I understand, being instructed by the Foreign Secretary, in the *strongest terms*, to give you every assistance in pursuit of your mission, to inform you of everything that will help you, and to smooth your way generally. That could be your trump

card. I've known the ambassador since he was plain Mr. Stratford
Canning; now, he's Viscount Stratford de Redcliffe, the great man in
Turkish affairs. He's highly thought of as a diplomat, not least by the
Russians, who can't stand him!'

'I'm not surprised,' remarked Mr. Brassey, with a chuckle, 'I'm
told he has a damned fiery temper.'

'Stratford has his arrogant side,' Mr. Peto admitted, 'but once his
sympathies are aroused he can be a powerful force—and his wife's
the same. If you can conquer at the Sublime Porte, Beatty, you may
find there will be far fewer obstacles in your path when you get to
Lord Raglan's headquarters.'

'I look forward to meeting this formidable ambassador,' I
replied, stoutly. 'I'm no diplomat, though, just a plain man of action.'

'That's perhaps what he will be hoping to find,' observed Mr.
Brassey. 'It may be your best passport to success.'

5

SOME DEPARTURES

Wednesday, 13th December

Smoke and steam rising from the gleaming locomotives, the familiar smell of warm oil, raucous greetings from navvies to their mates, a buzz of chatter up and down the long platform and, arching over all, as bright a sky as could be wished for on a winter morning. Such was the setting for the departure of our first trainload of men from the London-Birmingham terminus at Euston Square, bound for Liverpool and an outward passage to the Crimea, on 15th December.

The women's coloured shawls and the bright scarves of the children—darting in and out of the groups—and the bunting strung along the platform were all set off against the great sandstone mass of the station itself, with its Doric portico and pairs of pavilions, standing on the wide-open north side of the Square.

I was glad to be travelling with the party, to witness the memorable embarkation on *Wildfire*, and was in high expectation of a punctual start at 9 am. The men's new kits had been firmly tarpaulined down in the goods wagons attached to the train. Railway constables patrolled the platform in pairs, and vendors of food and drink were doing a roaring trade; all the children were clutching a toffee-apple or a twist of sweetmeats.

All this was in marked contrast to the scene at Victoria Station five days before, when I had seen Donald Campbell and his advance party off for Paris. That whole setting had seemed squalid: there was no station facade, sheds rose bleakly from behind a huddle of one-storey wooden buildings, vacant lots were disfigured by advertisement hoardings. Fog darkened every corner. Donald's and his party's piles of baggage had looked workmanlike enough, as I would have expected, but somewhat meagre for such an important assignment.

However, he had always preferred to travel light, I remembered.

His beloved mother had come to see him off, well wrapped-up against the evening chill. With her had stood the wives of John Wright, our aspiring assistant surveyor, and Henry Stone, best of draughtsmen—both important figures in the team.

As I shook Donald's hand he'd said simply: 'Don't you worry about anything, Jim. We'll get it all worked out and s-shipshape.'

'I'm sure of it, old friend,' I had replied. 'See you in Balaklava.'

Then, after last embraces and cries of 'Good luck,' the small party was quickly aboard—and off—precisely on time.

All hopes of an equally smooth start for us at Euston were soon blown away. A warning whistle from the engine brought an answering roar from a group of our men who were still scrumming around on the platform, not having yet signed their allotment papers in the waiting rooms we'd provided for the purpose. Though they were good-tempered, responding cheerfully to the unexpected air of carnival, there was no mistaking their determination to see everything in order before they set off. 'Better put the start back to ten o'clock,' I called to Bob Shaw, who was standing nearby, 'or there'll be a riot.'

It was gratifying to see the men's wholehearted response to our initiative: more than two-thirds were voluntarily making allocations of part of their pay. Whatever might sometimes be held against navvies for their drunkenness and fighting, no one could deny that such a gesture showed they could also shoulder responsibility. Earlier, several of the officers had, like me, made over their whole salaries to wives and families

Suddenly, advancing towards me, brisk and dapper as always, was Edward Ladd Betts. 'Hello, Beatty,' he cried, flourishing his cane, 'Slipped out of the office for a minute: couldn't miss the "off".' He swung round, taking in the scene. 'How does our Tennyson put it:

Let the great world spin for ever
Down the ringing grooves of change!

'That shows just how little he knew about locomotives' I said, tersely.

46

'You lack the poetic vision,' laughed Betts. 'Trouble is, we're both over-worked. I recommend oysters and a good navvy steak—nothing like it. Peto wanted to come,' he went on, 'but was nabbed by the Duke, who is, by the way, exceedingly happy the timetable is being followed so precisely.' Betts clapped me on the shoulder. 'Pleasant journey to Liverpool, Beatty—and back.' A flourish of his cane, and he was gone.

Shaw came over from the waiting-rooms, threading his way between the couples embracing tenderly along the length of the train. 'The last papers have just been signed,' he reported. 'Perhaps you should get into our compartment now, Mr. Beatty. I've put Dr. Howes, the new chief surgeon, in with us: he reported for duty yesterday afternoon, chirpy as if he were off on his honeymoon. The gangers are getting the men on board; then we're off.'

It was exactly ten o'clock. The guard, a tall, stern figure looking every inch as imposing as a regimental sergeant-major at the Queen's birthday parade, ceremoniously raised his flag. A bugle note sounded; porters flourished their caps; every engine in the station got up a deafening whistle. The long train drew away slowly, with two locomotives at the front to pull it up the tricky slope. The navvies, heads jammed out of every window, gave shout after shout, and then began to sing at the top of their voices:

> *Cheer, boys, cheer! No more of idle sorrow!*
> *Courage, true hearts, shall bear us on our way.*
> *Hope points before, and shows the bright tomorrow,*
> *Let us forget the darkness of today.*
>
> *Cheer, boys, cheer! For country, mother country.*
> *Cheer, boys, cheer! the willing strong right hand.*
> *Cheer, boys, cheer!...*

At length, a bend in the line carried our train out of sight of the crowd, and the men settled back in their seats, highly gratified to be going off in such style.

47

I relished every moment of that long journey north, bumpy as it was. We were launched on our adventure; Albert Howes more than lived up to my expectations after our first encounter at his dingy surgery, the day after he had handed in his letter for me at our temporary office. Was there, he had asked, any hope of a vacancy in the engineering corps for a medical man? 'I looked at your recruits, and thought I might just stand a chance. My tools of the trade match very well with your navvies' pickaxes.'

After graduating from King's College, London, Howes had quickly become disillusioned with his first post as a locum in a poor practice on the south side of the Thames. But he had an engaging touch of self-mockery that had appealed to me. I could imagine my father warming to his informal approach; so I had offered him the post of surgeon-in-chief at £500, plus rations. He had accepted on the spot, and undertook to find three assistant surgeons. He had also volunteered that he knew of four capable nurses: matronly, plump-looking women, was his description. 'In fact, straight up and down, if you know what I mean, but of a comforting appearance in a sick man's eyes.' I had been happy to leave him to those tasks which he had fulfilled admirably.

It was relaxing to jaw about medical matters, and I found myself telling stories of my childhood as the son of a country doctor, while we shared a picnic lunch which Sarah had thoughtfully packed. After that, nothing would satisfy him but to get down his kit of instruments from the luggage rack. All were of a pattern familiar to me, identical to those my father had started with as a young doctor in Enniskillen in 1812.

'My old man gave me these when I qualified,' said Howes. 'He had hopes of a career in the army for me, but there was no money in the family. Look at it—the complete standard issue used in all regimental hospitals. It's enough to put any normal man off surgery for life—not to mention the patient!'

A true enthusiast, he took me meticulously through his collection, lovingly handling each individual piece—saws, amputating knives, forceps, scalpels, needles, catheters—before finally strapping them away in their leather case. 'With these, and a few more bits and pieces, I can turn eye specialist and dentist as well.' He added, with a smile: 'Not to speak of doubling up as your regular pox doctor; I pride myself on taking the clap in my stride!'

Our arrival at Liverpool was a bitter anti-climax. Captain Downward, from *Wildfire*, took me aside at the ticket barrier.

'Glad to see you, sir, safe and sound,' he said, 'but I've bad news: you can guess what it is, no doubt.' He gestured up at the sky where black rain-clouds were streaming along in a biting north-westerly gale. 'We'll not be able to move the ship until this has blown itself out. I know this weather: lethal as hell when it's in this quarter. There's no possible way we'll get off on Friday.'

'Are you certain?' I asked. He nodded. 'I'm afraid so. Every Birkenhead sailing has been cancelled.' Downward had done his best: he'd fixed the navvies up in quarters ashore. Mr. Scott, for many years manager of our firm's shipping company, had taken rooms for me and the staff at the Sun Inn, and would be joining us in the morning to inspect the ship. The captain commented on Scott's 'enormous help' over the fitting out.

We had a noisy and disgruntled set of men on our hands that night, cast friendless on a storm shore. But Downward was right; waiting was all we could do. I wrote to warn Sarah I would have to stay on to see our first vessel off safely, and also sent a note to Kellock instructing him to finalise preparations for the departure of *Hesperus*, due out of Blackwall Dock at the end of the month. She, at all events, I thought, comforting myself, was a steam-ship!

But a sound sleep that night and a tolerable breakfast raised all our spirits despite the wind and slashing rain. 'Wait till you're aboard ship,' said Downward to Bob Shaw with a grin, 'then I'll show you what real sea-going grub tastes like.'

Scott, brimming with enthusiasm, took us at a brisk pace over the ship, eagerly pointing out all the changes that had been effected over the past few days. The men's quarters were roomy, if spartan, and the separate cabins for Bob Shaw and his colleagues were adequate enough. All construction stores and equipment, after rigorous checking by Scott and his assistant, had been swayed on board and stowed safely below. *Wildfire* herself was a new vessel with pleasing lines and a solid feel to her. Given a favourable wind it might just be possible, I thought, to make up the time lost and still reach Balaklava on time. I clung to that hope, tenaciously.

Downward's prediction turned out to be correct. For five days the gale blew viciously. Then, suddenly the wind shifted, the cloud cover began to break up and chinks of blue sky appeared. Clothes felt dry and more comfortable again and there was a feeling of anticipation in the air. Downward gave orders for *Wildfire* to be tugged to the dock gates in readiness for the start. The next day—21st December—would, he assured me, have a favourable tide around noon.

So that evening, representing the firm, I arranged a 'Grand Dinner' at Gough's Hotel, Woodside Ferry, to wish godspeed to all on the first ship in our armada. Along with our guests—a number of local notables—we made it a merry occasion. There were speeches, bumpers were drunk, and, I was told, the hotel had rarely heard such spirited singing.

Departure day dawned sharp and bright, with a soft, encouraging wind blowing white clouds across the blue sky. Shaw and the others were out early marshalling the men, many of whom had clearly had little if any sleep, but had been nevertheless determined to mark the occasion in style, and had been singing on and off since the early hours. That was a measure of how keyed up they were, for song had no place in normal working life where silence ruled, signifying each navvy's fierce desire to prove to his fellows that he was a true '20-ton-a-day' man and no shirker, however hard a stint might be.

An old favourite was repeated many times:

> *Oh, Judy, my dear, ye're young 'n' tender,*
> *When I'm away ye'll no' surrender,*
> *But hold out like an ancient Roman,*
> *And I'll make 'e an honest woman.*
> *So love, farewell!*

And, on a more martial note, a tune from the 88th Connaught Rangers:

We'll fight to the last
And no mortals we'll spare, me boys,
What better fun could ye ask
Than chasing the Bear, me boys?

As they formed into lines, the hastily-arranged military band took its place at the head of the procession. The bass drum gave a preliminary double-thump, and the singing changed abruptly to a cheer. Swirling flags and the brilliant uniforms of the bandsmen added splashes of colour, and a ray of sunshine caught the well-polished bugles. Shrill notes from the fifes bounced off the houses.

Bob Shaw's face was shining with pride as well as perspiration as he led his men briskly down Bridge Street to the dockside while bells were pealing from the tower of a nearby church. Spectators jammed windows and doors along the pot-holed road, saluting the navvies with shouts and huzzahs as they swaggered past, each dressed to kill with rainbow waistcoats and gaudy handkerchiefs. Some sported a velveteen coat and a white felt hat with turned-up brim.

This patriotic outburst was taken up by hundreds of other well-wishers, gathered expectantly in a semi-circle on the quayside. Once there, the band launched itself into a spirited rendering of popular songs: *Hey for the Life of a Soldier, Oh, Susannah* and *Auld Lang Syne,* leading inexorably back, time and time again, to *Cheer, Boys, Cheer,* the most popular of all. A bugle called the end of each verse, with extra rolls on the side drums and runs on the fifes for the choruses.

Now came the moment the men had been waiting for: the high-piled wagon-loads of their personal kits were positioned alongside the gangway, and the protective tarpaulins were flung back. As though on cue, an imposing carriage drew up at the head of our procession. Out stepped the Duke of Newcastle, tall and bearded, accompanied by Mr. Peto and two officials. The Duke greeted me affably as I introduced Downward, Scott and Shaw.

'I determined on being here with you gentlemen at this momentous departure,' said the Duke. 'As it happens, I was not free to come on the 15th, so this delay has worked well for me, though it must have been exceedingly irksome for you, after all the toil and preparation.'

'*Wildfire* is reputed a fast clipper,' I said. 'Captain Downward tells me he is confident of making up lost time during the voyage. At least, the men have been spared several days of seasickness.'

'When do you expect to arrive at Balaklava, Captain?' asked the Duke, gazing with admiration at the sparkling new ship, dressed overall.

'At the very beginning of February, sir; sooner, with luck,' replied Downward.

'Capital! I wish *Wildfire* a most speedy passage. Now, tell me, Beatty, what are your own plans?'

'I shall be travelling overland to Marseilles as soon as possible, my Lord; and, after a brief stop at Constantinople, Balaklava by mid-January. It is the route my advance party—Donald Campbell's all-important survey team—took nearly a fortnight ago; so they should soon be at work. After that, it will be full steam ahead.' I caught the Duke's nod of approbation to Mr. Peto, and decided to risk a 'flyer'. 'While I'm in Constantinople I'm meeting our Ambassador: I'll be looking for advice on the latest conditions at the front.'

'Ah, yes, our Lord Stratford,' replied the Duke, giving me a keen look. 'Indeed, he usually has something of weight to impart about most things.' He turned to Mr. Peto. 'You've kept to your targets admirably so far. I look forward to seeing the railway at work within three weeks of the navvies' arrival—your promise, eh?'

'I'm completely confident of it, Minister,' replied Mr. Peto, calmly.

'The Government will be very glad to have that assurance,' replied the Duke, 'and so am I.' The Opposition may perhaps be wishing for a different outcome, but—' he broke off to glance at the wagons. 'Tell me, what are those large bundles being unloaded from the trucks?'

'Tarpaulins, my Lord. We use them to protect our men till they can get their wooden huts up.'

'You take that much trouble?' exclaimed the Duke. 'What a good thing it would be if some of these could be sent out for our wretched soldiers who have to sleep on the bare ground!'

'I could get you any number you wish in two or three days, my Lord,' replied Mr. Peto.

'You are infinitely obliging, my dear Peto. Thank you, I'll consult the Ordnance Department as a matter of urgency—of extreme urgency.'

(Two months later, Betts, in a private letter to me, alluded to this matter of the tarpaulins. The Duke had indeed enquired, he told me, but Ordnance considered the proceedings 'too irregular', so the matter was allowed to drop!)

To stirring music, the navvies formed into a boarding party. Each man carried his bed up the gangplank; then returned for the issue of a personal kit, the last item of which was a large leather belt to hold their belongings together. In a few minutes, all gear was signed for, taken aboard and carried below.

As the empty wagons rumbled slowly away, the spectators surged quickly forward to get a closer view.

So, Love, Farewell, the band played, as a tug manoeuvred into position at the bow of the ship and dockers began to cast off the hawsers.

All eyes were fixed on her topmast where a long pennant was being unfurled. This distinguishing flag was, on War Office orders, to be flown by every ship in our armada. The Admiralty, for its part, had instructed the chief naval engineers at Gibraltar, Malta and the Dardanelles to speed our vessels on their way 'by every means in their power.'

Just then, a group of navvies burst out on to the deck, flaunting their new red flannel shirts, pea-jackets, moleskin trousers and mufflers, waving, singing and shouting. Some had donned their sou'westers and long waterproof boots, and two inveterate jokers clambered up into the rigging, to everyone's amusement.

Bob Shaw was quick to get the show-offs down on deck, and immediately, all the men crowded to the rails, banging picks and shovels, and loudly chanting 'Down wi' the bloody Roosians!'

I must have stood there for a moment, day-dreaming about our armada and our mission, for when I looked up, *Wildfire* was drawing quietly away from the quayside. She was swiftly joined by a Government emigrant vessel, which gave a loud greeting. Mingled cheers from both ships echoed across the water. As we watched, the clipper's sails filled and, with her long pennant streaming aloft, she drove through a choppy sea as the light brightened by the minute.

* * * * * * *

Close on midnight I reached home, to be greeted at the front door by Sarah, in tears.

'Oh, thank God you're back, Jim,' she sobbed, clutching me closely. 'The Old Doctor—your father—has died.'

'My father? When?'

'Last Sunday, it seems—the 17th. Lizzy's telegram didn't get here until yesterday: I didn't know what to do.'

I sat, stunned, in the still-warm parlour. My father, Dr. James—the Old Doctor—dead! When I'd seen him at my sister's house in Corkhill in the summer he had certainly been ailing a little, but able to relish the comfort of his armchair, his pipe and the copies of *The Times* we sent over regularly. At sixty-nine, he had still had a grip on life. But now, dead... my mind blurred.

Sarah was repeating a remark she'd obviously made several times already: 'I couldn't bear to give you this dreadful news while you were in Liverpool, away from home.'

Home was the one focus, the only thing to hold on to—dearest Sal, her baby still to be born, and our three precious chicks. I searched for her warm steadying hand, and gripped it tightly. 'You were right,' I said. 'Yesterday, that news would have destroyed me.' I had an instantaneous picture of the last few days, and relived the strain of events. Now, I had yet another responsibility—head of the family.

'You did absolutely right,' I whispered to Sarah, who was still standing silent by my side, her hand clasped in mine. She was bare-footed, in a nightdress over which she had flung a dressing-gown. 'There was nothing I could have done, my love, even if I had known. There was no getting away earlier.'

Next morning I wakened from a restless sleep to see Sarah beside the bed. She handed me a letter: I knew the handwriting: it took only a minute to read:

The Office
21st December '54

Dear Beatty

Short notice, as usual. I've secured passages for you and your party of three on L'Hirondelle, *a troopship sailing ex Marseilles for Constantinople on 28th December.*

I'm afraid this will mean crossing from Dover on Christmas Day, but can't risk any delay on the French railways. Do look in as soon as you get back: I'm in all day.

Best regards to Mrs. Beatty
Yours, E.L.B.

PS I am truly sorry about the unfestive timing.

Sarah gave an anguished cry. My own feeling was of dull grief. It would be a Christmas of rushed farewells: only a private prayer would mark the Old Doctor's funeral in Enniskillen.

Determined to put such sad thoughts aside, Sarah and I threw ourselves hectically into my last three days in England. Clothes were packed and re-packed—the addition of a Panama to the pile prompted one of our rare laughs. I parcelled up my set of instruments, assembled a box of basic medicines, and picked out some precious books to read on board ship. Sarah produced notepaper and envelopes: 'You won't find those in the Crimea,' she remarked, practically. We made endless—and unsuccessful—attempts to reduce the number of boxes and trunks. Finally, all were strapped up and conspicuously labelled, twice over for luck. Henry turned up trumps, writing conscientiously to all members of our families who would together be bearing the brunt of the funeral arrangements and the settlement of my father's estate.

When I went in to the office after receiving Betts' note, he was touchingly understanding. I was presented with a fine Bible by Mr. Peto, who came in with Mr. Brassey to wish me Godspeed. Betts pressed a box of fine cigars on me.

I was amused to be treated with some ceremony at the Foreign Office when I went to collect the Earl of Clarendon's personal letter of introduction to Lord Stratford. From one of the under-secretaries I gleaned a few scraps of information about the ambassador's style at the Sublime Porte. They bore out the impression I had gained of his character from my colleagues: autocratic, hot-tempered... Well, we would see.

Christmas Day burst on 13 Blomfield Terrace with more spontaneity and laughter than I had somehow expected; there were also moments for quiet thanksgiving, as well as presents. Fanny and Susy, in their best dresses and party shoes, with red ribbons in their hair, were giddy with excitement.

Lunch was early, and a trifle subdued. I caught Sarah's gaze more than once resting pensively on me: was she remembering perhaps that Christmas in Nova Scotia with our then one month old Wallace, when Donald Campbell and I had ridden in on horseback from camp through a blizzard, for a first glimpse of the boy?

'I wonder where Donald is now,' she remarked quietly, as we tucked the children up for their usual sleep before setting off for Victoria Station.

'He'll have reached Balaklava by now,' I replied. 'A big moment for him—his first detached command.'

'He's a good man,' exclaimed Sarah. 'I'm so thankful you two will be out there together. I told him so before he left.'

'What did he say?' I asked, somewhat taken aback.

'He started to stammer; but he was moved, you could see.'

All too quickly it was time to leave for the station. Henry summoned a brougham, and we all piled in, the girls over-awed by the grandeur of the carriage. All too soon the unlovely buildings and tattered hoardings loomed up, and at last we reached the almost empty platform deep in shadow, and the train bound for Dover.

I found it agonising to break away from Sarah and the girls and step up into the train with Henry. The other two members of our little party—our servants William Ayling and his younger brother Robert—had a compartment further along the train and were being seen off by a huge family group in boisterous mood as if setting off on a picnic. At twenty-one and nineteen years of age—and unmarried— who could blame the youngsters for their high spirits?

Sarah, tears pouring down her cheeks, and I held hands tightly through the open window, silently watching Fanny and Susy hopping and skipping unconcernedly at her side. Henry quietly stowed away our travelling bags on the racks.

The whistle blew. 'God take care of you, my darling,' I whispered. As our train drew out and I lost sight of my loved ones, I pulled up the window and sat heavily down beside my brother-in-law. Not much was said between us until the train steamed into the welcome lights of Dover, precisely on time. I took that as an auspicious omen. Please God it would prove so!

6

THE SUBLIME PORTE

26ᵗʰ December

Our little party reached Paris at noon, exhausted by a vile Channel crossing, and we left by train for Marseilles—a seventeen-hour journey—later in the day. A Boxing Day to remember for a long time, especially those hours I spent on deck encouraging a very seasick Henry. I couldn't get out of my mind the sight of Sal's sad face at Victoria Station, and her final brave attempt at a smile, while urging the little girls to wave me good-bye.

Arriving in Marseilles, cramped, cold and hungry, at 5 pm the next day, we put up at the Hotel des Colonies close to the docks. As we drove next morning down the crowded waterfront streets to our ship, we had a good view of the impressive Grande Joliette—one of a series of new basins going up round the great natural anchorage. Our ship, though, was a bit of a let-down: a solid, weathered old French trooper, whose twin funnels and upperworks hadn't seen paint for years. The scene was chaotic. Last-minute cargo was being loaded: soldiers were streaming up the gangways to join those already packing the decks. Nothing could have been a greater contrast to the departure of the tiny *Wildfire* earlier in the month. Our navvies, though brawny, would have been instantly lost in the huge crowd that swarmed all over the decks—Zouaves and Legionnaires colourfully conspicuous, everyone gesticulating and jabbering at once in thick patois. I decided then and there to take lessons in metropolitan French: the little lingo I had picked up in Canada would certainly not suffice for any serious conversations I could find myself engaged in with Allied military officers I might encounter in the Crimea.

The whole scene was of flamboyant cheerfulness; the smoke from the foreign tobacco was rank in my nostrils and even the cigars smelled different. An artillery band on the after-deck played us stirringly out of harbour. Inhaling the salt-laden air I suddenly had a sense of being part of a gigantic adventure, and responded with almost boyish enthusiasm!

But my lasting memory of *L'Hirondelle* was of a very badly-managed ship: the standard of cooking was abysmal and the cool impudence of her crew passed all bounds. Heaven forgive me, I thought, if ever I travelled on a French vessel again if I could get an English one. However, the captain, after a day or two, showed himself to be a gentlemanly sort of fellow—for a Frenchman.

Among the thirty or so officers on board I was happy to discover several British gunners. A Captain Hall from Monaghan turned out to be a great friend of one of Sarah's relatives, Mrs. Maguire, and he also knew Mrs. Sheppard well, as a near neighbour. Henry fell in with a group of young Irish surgeons and spent all day larking with them. Among them was a Dr. Madden from Dublin, and Mr. Roche, of Waterford. One cheerful fellow, whom I took to instantly, was Dr. Walsh: I was glad he was going on to Balaklava with us.

Hosts of battle-hardened passengers were laid low during our unpleasant passage to Malta. To distract my mind I practised my French on an obliging young infantry lieutenant but we both acknowledged that my grammar was a stumbling block, and he agreed to give me daily lessons till we reached Constantinople. It was a relief just to struggle into Valetta harbour on New Year's Day, released at last from the battering of wind and wave.

Next morning, Henry and I breakfasted in some style at the English Hotel in St. Ursula Street, admiring the extravagant festoons of ramparts and fortifications. Then and there I made a New Year resolution: to keep a daily diary. I had tried once before in Nova Scotia but conditions were too rough for the maintenance of a continuous record. This time, I determined to keep a blow-by-blow account, not only of the unfolding of historic events but also of my own reactions and assessments of colleagues and the mysterious military I would be dealing with. Personalities did not easily reveal their true colours on a first chance encounter. We all liked to think we were special: a diary might prove a sieve to trap the exceptional man. My thoughts went to Donald Campbell who would now, I was confident, be working flat-out on our all-important route. He, like our soldiers, was the unsung hero of our venture. That thought was the first entry in my diary—written with a scratchy pen on a lined pad I had picked up on the Paris station. Actually, I bought three, which was just as well for there was little chance of replenishments as we went east. Our captain decided to make a dash for it, but after four hours sea and wind had again defeated us roundly, and we lay at anchor off Malta, tossing about all night. All in all, I confided to my diary, I had never in my life experienced such a disruptive week. But it was a very salutary preparation for Balaklava: no campaign on *terra firma* could be more disagreeable.

I wrote a second letter to Sarah, in an attempt to concentrate on homely matters, and crowd out of my mind the abominable racket outside the cabin and the menacing thud of waves against the side of the old trooper. By then I had had time to go through my personal baggage, and found to my dismay that, despite most careful packing, I had included many unwanted items in two tightly-crammed trunks I had meant to leave in our Paddington loft! More annoyingly, I did not appear to have my new mahogany box of spare instruments and my valued silver-inlaid pencil case.

I asked Sarah to purchase a replacement from Farthings, of 42 Cornhill Street, and also a common box and pencils to stow into it. Our shippers in King William Street would forward the lot, including my rifle once it had been overhauled by Dean and Adams. On a more personal note before the rising hubbub made a coherent account of anything impossible, I copied out the diary entry I had just made:

> *I trust to a merciful God to give me health and strength to get through the labour and difficulties of my position which I will not conceal from you are very great. In fact I have got a responsibility that nothing but energy and perseverance will enable me to get through with honour and advantage.*

Snow and sleet blew us down the length of the Mediterranean: each day was uniformly unpleasant. Nevertheless, I persisted with basic French lessons under my tutor—unpaid, but not averse to an occasional cigar with his cognac. Even when *L'Hirondelle* dropped in briefly at one of the Grecian islands, Khios, and we ventured ashore, torrential rain blotted out all views.

As the ship approached Smyrna the clouds lifted, and snow-covered mountains appeared. The high hinterland looked barren and inhospitable but right down to the shoreline there were cypresses and thick groves of olive trees, interspersed with neat red-roofed white houses. Smyrna, the traditional birthplace of Homer, lay elegantly around the blue waters of Korfezi Bay, backed by a noble peak. Who could have imagined that ten days after leaving England I would be thus plunged into Asia? A longing for travel surged strongly in me— to run over to Jerusalem and heaven knows where else. However, in two more days I would be in Constantinople, and then heading unwaveringly north to the Crimea.

While we steamed across an unusually placid Sea of Marmara towards the Golden Horn I put daydreams aside,and tried to gather my thoughts for the forthcoming meeting with our ambassador to the Sublime Porte. Much could depend on it and, from what I had gathered so far, Lord Stratford de Redcliffe sounded anything but an amiable character. Yet, he had been instructed by the Foreign Secretary, Lord Clarendon, to give me 'every assistance in his power', and I carried also a personal letter of introduction. In Turkey, Lord Stratford wielded great influence and had championed British interests in the region successfully over many years. His honorific title 'The Great Elchi' (Great Envoy) indicated the ascendancy he had attained in ruling circles, and notably with the Turkish Sultan, Abdul Medjid.

But I was unknown, and the term 'assistance' was an elastic one, capable of infinite interpretations, particularly in the mind of an experienced diplomat. I must somehow succeed in gaining his personal interest and cooperation in my expedition.

What sort of man, I wondered, would I find? Only a states-manlike mask; or perhaps someone of understanding who would appreciate the picks and shovels of my navvy gangs for what they really were—implements to clear away all obstacles for a supreme cause? Time would tell, and there was little left.

I sat, mulling over my notes in the small, dark cabin Henry and I were sharing, while listening to the loud voices and footsteps echoing down the corridor outside. On one thing I was determined: I would *not* be patronised by His Excellency, and certainly not by any Turkish grandee, and I would be on my guard against accepting any offer of support that seemed less than wholehearted from anyone.

The captain told me confidently on the morning of 8th January that we should be dropping anchor at Constantinople in a few hours. I went on deck but could see nothing, and shortly came below, discouraged by a drenching rainstorm that had obviously set in for the day. Nevertheless, considering the season of the year, ours had been a remarkably swift passage. I wrote a note to Sarah telling her I was feeling fit and itching to get to Balaklava to help mitigate the sufferings of the army; and urged her to trust, as I did, in a merciful God for my continued health.

I put on a sou'wester and cap before going back on deck to catch my first glimpse of the fabled city—mosques and minarets towering into the sky, a Bosphorus and Golden Horn crowded with shipping. That was not only my dream: it seemed as though every one of the ship's passengers was of a similar mind. We were all disappointed: even our band were driven to packing their instruments away against the driving rain. Highly-coloured craft of all sizes were swarming around, offering wicker baskets, food, trinkets; but our minds were set on getting ashore. William and Robert had dumped our baggage strategically near a gangway and were guarding it fiercely until we were ready to disembark.

The real eye-opener came as we picked our way to a hotel through narrow streets pitted with filthy puddles and littered with half-eaten carcasses of dogs and mules that smelled villainously. In our upstairs room Henry and I were wakened throughout the night by the barking of wild dogs and the howling of scavenging cats in the street below. How I longed to be back at home! An incongruous sight we saw at dinner each day was that of two English ladies, each with a husband serving in the Crimea, and both trying hard to convince themselves that, at least, they were near those they loved. Yet their privations were truly great and their circumstances extraordinary by any standard. Having no family constituted their sole justification for being there. One could only feel sorry for such a sad, stranded couple of women.

I felt sorry for myself, too, and fretted endlessly at every delay, though none was of my own making. I made trip after fruitless trip to the British Embassy before managing to arrange an interview with Lord Stratford—three days hence. The news from the front grew more alarming by the day. It was clear I would arrive at Balaklava not a moment too soon. All troops were enduring unspeakable hardship. All system had broken down. Seas of mud had made the few tracks unusable by mules. Rations, and every item of clothing, had to be transported the five or six miles from Balaklava to the exposed camps on the plateau on the backs of the men; even the officers, their uniforms in tatters, were forced to hump bundles of firewood and any small luxuries that might have arrived for them by ship from England.

I had 'bread and salt' feelings as I gazed on the scene. On one side of the Bosphorus was Constantinople, city of the sultans, with thousands of years of history behind it; on the other lay Scutari with its vast Barrack Hospital, housing thousands of our soldiers wounded in battles in support of a people that reviled them as unbelievers.

I crossed the Bosphorus by ferry on the Tuesday afternoon to see the place for myself, following an invitation from an old Enniskillen acquaintance, Dr. Bobby Hudson. He met Henry and me with ponies at the landing place, a marble quay from which steps led up to a high terrace surmounted by an elegant mosque, It had been built, Bobby told us, four centuries before and was known as the Mosque of the Waterside. Bobby, I was amused to note, had adopted the 'moustache' movement which he obviously felt gave his short tubby frame a quasi-military air. He was affable enough, but I found his off-hand manner jarring as he showed us round. One could only gaze at the gaunt hospital building in unbelieving silence. It had until recently been a Turkish barracks; against its dilapidated exterior were still heaped huge piles of stinking rubbish and excrement.

Miss Florence Nightingale and her 38 nurses had arrived on the *Verity* only on 4th November; since then they had been working night and day to bring about some order, and nursing care, to the sick and wounded. Over 3,000 patients had been taken in already, which, as Bobby remarked with complacency, was more than five times the number to be found in the largest military hospital in England.

Two streams of men were attempting to use the main entrance simultaneously: one detail carrying out the dead for burial; the other, struggling to bring in the latest intake of men, some who were visibly dying on their stretchers. Inside, the fetid wards presented a spectacle from hell. Blood-stained pallets lay packed close on the floors. One soldier died as I paused at his side. The mortality was appalling. Bobby mentioned losing 30-40 men a day from cholera, typhus and dysentery. From a cursory glance around I would have doubled that total. The few chaplains were completely rushed off their feet. One told me that if he once lost sight of a patient he would never find him again: his place on the blanket would have instantly been taken by another sufferer—only the old name-tag would remain, and be recorded over and over.

All the old hulks for wounded in the harbour were full. It was rumoured that the English ambassador was seeking to requisition a Turkish cavalry barracks at Kullali nearby. Would it be sufficient, and in time?

Miss Nightingale's arrival had galvanised everybody, but the needs were overpowering, and past mismanagement could not be rectified in a day. This lady had been accompanied on her mission of mercy by an English gentleman, Mr. Bracebridge, and his wife. He told me an astonishing story. An aristocrat, Lady Blackwood, had arrived in Scutari in December with her medical husband on missionary service, and had begged an appointment with Miss Nightingale. 'I will do anything,' she declared. 'Do you mean that?' 'Yes.' 'In that case,' said Miss Nightingale, 'I have a job for you.' She showed her a dark cellar in the main building over-flowing with sick and dying army wives for whom no medical provision of any kind had been made. Lady Blackwood had since worked ceaselessly in that squalid place; babies were still being born there; some that would not have survived, have lived. I felt thankful that my own chicks had had at least a far happier start, and that our expedition was bringing out its own medical and nursing team.

I started out early next afternoon for my appointment with Lord Stratford, with the temperature dropping sharply and an icy wind gusting about my ears. The streets in both directions were jammed with horses and carts, mules and the occasional bedraggled camel. It was hard work shouldering a way through the crowds that spilled out from the pavements: Turks, Greeks, Armenians, beggars and evil-looking Bashi Bazooks with knives and antique pistols stuck in their waistbands. Merchants were pouring in and out of cramped business houses; in the dark alleys children were fighting and crying.

The rebuilt Embassy was pleasantly situated off a square half way along the narrow Grande Rue de Pera where most of the other embassies were to be found, cheek by jowl with more traditional commercial premises and new European-style apartments, all with wrought-iron balconies covered with bare vine branches.

Passing through the entrance and being greeted by courteous staff in a wide palm court was like entering a different world. Lord Stratford was concluding a meeting; I was offered coffee by one of his personal staff who pointed out with pride the new 'English' garden that was being constructed at the rear of the building. The tossing branches of the bare trees had the forlorn look of a typical February day back home. 'It will be a picture in the spring,' remarked the secretary, 'though one can never rely on settled weather: it's sun one minute, then snow or a hurricane, followed by sleet.' The garden was apparently the creation of a Mr. Allison, who until his recent promotion to our embassy in Persia had been the Oriental Secretary here. He had been much esteemed for his prodigious command of eastern languages and even more for the quiet and witty way in which he was able to soften the ambassador's darker moods. Lord Stratford, the secretary confided to me, enjoyed few distractions from his heavy labours. He had frequently been found in the morning still in evening dress, having worked on correspondence right through the night.

Finally I was led up a grand staircase and through the first-floor ballroom to Lord Stratford's book-lined office overlooking the garden. He was writing at a large roll-top desk. As I came in it seemed to me that he rose to his feet a trifle wearily, but his greeting was cordial enough, and he motioned me to a sofa near the window. A servant immediately began to pour Turkish coffee into two small cups on a low table between the ambassador and myself. It was too late to refuse, but Lord Stratford had noticed my half-gesture and smiled.

'Be patient, Mr. Beatty,' he remarked. 'Long years of service in this country have habituated me to the custom of frequent coffee drinking, accompanied by a glass of water, preparatory to any serious talk. I have found it invaluable in settling both my mind and my stomach.'

We sipped our coffee amicably in silence, and I had a chance to study this singular man who did not appear nearly as over-bearing in manner as I had expected. He was tall and well-built, in an immaculate suit, but his movements though deliberate had an air of suppressed energy. One could perhaps imagine him erupting in anger; on the other hand his remarkable stillness might have been merely an affectation, a kind of vanity used to overawe those around him. From an inner pocket he took the letter of introduction I had brought from Lord Clarendon. 'I have read the Foreign Secretary's personal note, but I should tell you that earlier I had an urgent dispatch from him on which I have been trying to act before your arrival.' This remark was said with a wry smile, but there had been a certain warmth in his voice that somehow raised my spirits. Could this man really be the imperious dragon everyone had warned me about?

'I emphasised *trying* to act,' he continued, 'and until the conclusion of my last meeting just now I believed that my attempted intervention might have yielded a constructive result. But men are no more malleable, Mr. Beatty, than mules.'

Knowing Lord Raglan's chronic manpower position, he had decided, on his own authority, to engage 800 local Croat labourers as a civilian force to assist me at Balaklava. However, their spokesman had finally announced that the men refused to go. 'They are discomforted by the weather,' said Lord Stratford, 'and also the state of things in the Crimea. One could hardly blame them, I suppose, though I offered high wages—high certainly by Croat standards.' With a slight smile he added: '*Croats* is how they are termed in common parlance: they're actually Asiatic subjects of the Sultan. I agree, that does not add up to any practical support for you, Mr. Beatty. I can only apologise for my obvious lack of persuasive power.'

I told him frankly that I had never envisaged getting any assistance of that kind from him, nor indeed to any extent from the army, except in the very early stages. I explained that I was bringing my own labour force and skilled staff from England: they were now on the way. He nodded and said he had read the newspaper reports, and quite took my point. 'Of course,' he said 'people in this country and climate could never be expected to work with the spirit and energy of your brawny navvies, but they might, I thought, be useful for rough work. You have not yet seen the reality of Balaklava, Mr. Beatty.'

'This "reality" is what I am hoping to learn from you, my Lord. Perhaps I could outline the plan as I see it now?' I did so as forcefully as I could, stressing that the advance guard of our armada of 23 ships would soon be arriving. Each vessel would bring both men and materials to avoid any hold up of the construction programme I had laid down. Nothing would stop me from driving that plan through, I ended emphatically.

I could see Lord Stratford gazing at me appraisingly. 'I admire your resolve, Mr. Beatty,' he said. 'Let me tell you a story. When I first came to this country, a slightly younger man than you, I found myself suddenly the acting ambassador at a difficult stage in negotiations involving us, Turkey and Russia. In the absence of any guidance—for the Foreign Office had quite forgotten my existence—I had no alternative but to steer by my own stars. Sometimes I still managed to pursue my own case—and win, even after official instructions eventually arrived.' Some years later, he continued, he was again back in Turkey, dealing with another set of problems, that time concerning Greece as well as Russia. 'On that occasion the plan I set out and fought for ardently failed completely. Why? Because of the personalities of the two leaders with whom I had to deal: the then Sultan Mahmud was by nature a caliph and a despot; the Russian emperor had decided I was hostile to his country's interests and declared me *persona non grata*. Even to achieve the slightest compromise I had to use the most intemperate language. Ever since, I have been noted for a hot temper. All due to my distaste for lying and unscrupulous potentates.

'Don't be dismayed by my experience—or inexperience. One must have a master plan, and urge it on, but planning has to take account of the participants: that is vital for success. On Queen Victoria's birthday on 24th May last year, a grand review of all troops had been staged at Pera. At the finale the bands of all the Allies struck up our national anthem; unfortunately they all played it in different keys!' Lord Stratford laughed at the memory: 'One tune, five keys—a sure recipe for disaster, especially with Allies.

'You'll find many worse calamities facing you in the Crimea, Mr. Beatty. Balaklava is unbelievably small, more like a tiny Scottish tarn than a proper port equipped to supply the needs of a whole army. Both British and French headquarters are on the plateau, but they are physically separated by a deep ravine, with no direct line of communication. I admire Lord Raglan's capabilities, but he is being ground down by ceaseless instructions from Whitehall, the lack of experienced generals and even competent staff officers. He is plagued, too, by an Ally dancing only to the tune of a distant, wayward emperor.

'To tell the truth, I find myself increasingly oppressed by the catastrophic loss of soldiers' lives and the seeming inability of our Government to provide reinforcements of seasoned troops. Thank God, you bring your own people with you. I admire you; we need a man of your nerve here.'

With great seriousness he added: 'I will back you, Mr. Beatty, if you stick to your plan. Provide your railway as promised *on time*; that will silence all critics. Write privately to me: please regard me as an ally-in-waiting.'

The servant proffered fresh coffee; Lord Stratford waved it away and stood up. The interview was over. As we were walking back through the ballroom he told me of a recent proclamation from the French emperor which had amused him. It was addressed to his troops in the Crimea, and ran: 'Your fathers, fighting under my uncle, were attacked by the plague. Be comforted: you have only cholera. Try to keep your feet dry and warm. Take care of your health. Mine is very good. Biarritz is a nice place of residence, but I shall soon join my army and share its labours.' He laughed, 'Bonaparte III has still not arrived: one has to be grateful for the smallest mercy!'

As we shook hands at the head of the grand staircase a lady emerged from an adjoining room. 'My dear,' Lord Stratford called out, 'may I present Mr. Beatty? He is come to carry out important work for Mr. Brassey and his associates.'

'Mr. *Thomas* Brassey?' enquired Lady Stratford. 'I have not the pleasure of his acquaintance, but when I was in London two years ago with my daughters I called twice on his wife—a most agreeable lady. She was interested to hear of the support my husband was then giving to Mr. Layard in his fascinating excavations at Nineveh. You must forgive me now: I am on my way to see Miss Nightingale at Scutari; but perhaps you are free to dine with my husband and our family here this evening? I should like to hear more of your project.'

'Sadly, ma'am, no; I am to leave tonight for Balaklava. You spoke of Scutari. A doctor friend took me round the wards there yesterday; the suffering was a thousand times worse than the epidemic that swept my home town of Enniskillen when I was a boy. My father was medical superintendent of the cholera hospital during those harrowing years: I remember well how it aged him.'

'Your father must have been a courageous man,' exclaimed Lady Stratford.

'He was determined to win the battle, that's for sure, ma'am,' I replied.

The ambassador and his wife watched as I descended the stairs. At the bottom I looked up; both raised a hand in friendly farewell. Then Lord Stratford turned slowly away back to his office.

With my mind in turmoil I walked back through the icy streets to our hotel, to be greeted by Henry with the news that he had seen our baggage safely stowed on the steamer *Sprite* and that we were due aboard within the hour.

The letter I wrote to my beloved Sal before we cast off in the deepening twilight, was, I'm ashamed to say, a proper rag-bag. I told her of my meeting with Bobby Hudson at Scutari; of the importunity of beggars in the Stamboul bazaars; of a chance encounter with a man from Halifax whose daughter was married to an officer of the First Royals, and of our great jaw about Nova Scotia. Finally, I begged her to write to Cole and Son, Bridge Street, Westminster, asking them to look out a hat for me, box it and hand it to the King William Street forwarders. I said I thought it would add much to my respectability! I mentioned my regret at not having brought more tea out with me, but said, DV, I meant to put up with the same rations as the men: they would be sufficient, though rough. My next letter, I promised, would give her details from the actual seat of war—but strictly only of what I observed myself.

My letter went safely ashore with the pilot launch; then Henry and I were in the saloon for a welcome meal. The last leg of a momentous voyage was beginning.

7

A MISERLY LITTLE TOWN

18th January 1855

Our three-day trip in *Sprite* from Constantinople across the Black Sea
had been uneventful though surprisingly rough for a so-called tideless
ocean. We drove on endlessly through steep waves blown into continuous white caps by a ferocious wind from the north. I was
consumed with anxiety to see once more the familiar figure of Donald
Campbell and hear his news, and spent the last morning of the voyage
on deck in what shelter I could find, scouring the approaching
landmass through a glass. It was impossible to detect any entrance to
Balaklava harbour along the cliffs that towered several hundred feet
into the air along that bleak coast. Only after we had inched past
Castle Point and swung cautiously round into the port did I catch my
first glimpse of him, standing on a cart at the quayside, both arms
waving vigorously aloft. Even at that distance he looked a mountain
of a man, with his huge woollen cap, oilskins and thigh boots. I could
just make out our draughtsman, Henry Stone, standing beside him.

Then a driving snowstorm blotted them out. I dived below
with a vivid impression of a minute harbour, little larger than a
decent-sized mill pond, yet crowded with the finest steam vessels
in the world, crammed together like spoons in a kitchen drawer.
Like the steep surrounding hills, all their decks were covered in the
thick snow which was also clinging to yards and rigging. Gleaming
icicles hung from the main spar. The buildings in the town were
largely invisible; understandably there were few people about. It
looked a wilderness of a place. I was glad to get below to the
comparative comfort of the saloon where Dr. Walsh greeted me
with the smiling relief of one for whom a painful experience was
over: his next steps would, he laughed, at least be on *terra firma*—

unconcerned that his final stop would be a remote field hospital.

Before he became too seasick he had amused us by quoting from a memoir written by an English lady long resident in the Crimea in days of peace. Her recollections of a vanished way of life was in stark contrast to the howl of an almost horizontal gale and the incessant slapping of waves against our portholes. One vignette she had painted stuck in my memory: the venerable head of a flourishing Tartar spending his last days puffing contentedly at his chibouk in the sunshine, squatting at the foot of the huge walnut tree that yielded the annual income for his whole family. A true Garden of Eden—a far cry indeed from earlier times in the region when the original Tartar inhabitants had been driven out by Greek pirates. Excused military service by Catherine the Great, they had finally settled down to a farming life of a kind, to supplement their pickings from piracy.

While we were still on board *Sprite* I added recklessly to my household stores by buying three tablecloths from the second officer, undeterred by the fact that his name was prominently embroidered on the corners. They had a somewhat calico look about them but were a definite luxury. All part of keeping one's end up, or so I argued—just harmless vanity!

No sooner had we moored than Donald came aboard, his glasses steamed up on his cheerful face, relieved and delighted to see us safely arrived. Stone padded along behind him with his canvas bag of engineering drawings and sketches which he pulled out to order. At first from sheer excitement Donald stammered away like smoke, but fortified by mugs of tea and freshly-baked bread, he eventually quietened down and told us his tale, thawing out at a corner table in the saloon.

He skipped over the outward passage: 'It was h-horrendous,' he said, 'quite the worst in my experience.' A breakdown on the French railways meant that the party had missed their intended fast steamer from Marseilles and were put on a Spanish tramper from Barcelona carrying a cargo of mules. Most of these and their muleteers were perpetually seasick. Food and quarters were equally rough, but on arrival he and his party started non-stop surveying. 'Our worst enemy, like Napoleon's, was "General Winter",' said Donald. He had tried to make early contact with the Board of Officers, the army body responsible for harbour organisation, along with a fiery-tempered Admiral Boxer, acting for the navy, whose self-proclaimed motto was: 'I'm bloody Boxer; I'm in charge and you'll do as I say.'

To Donald's relief, naval responsibility for the harbour had soon been turned over to Captain Heath, of HMS *Sanspareil*, who though equally forthright was much less abrasive. He instantly grasped the significance of the railway and keenly watched Wright's daily progress with theodolite and measuring chains. 'I had to dodge him in the end,' Donald confessed. 'Like all the rest, he would keep enquiring when the chief would be arriving and construction actually begin.'

He had found the Board's approach lackadaisical and erratic: it had taken several days to fix a first meeting, and another couple to agree that the Civil Engineering Corps' base should be located at the Ordnance Wharf. Donald had to argue strongly for this because of its deep water and a promising space to the east that could be cleared for a railway yard, and for plant and equipment to be stacked. Stables for the horses could also be erected there next to the Commissary-General's office and stores.

Donald pointed out on one of Stone's sketch-maps a little hill further back which, he considered, would, when levelled and banked, make a convenient site for navvies' huts and a store shed. Beyond, hills rose almost perpendicularly. He had looked at the western edge of the harbour. Though it appeared unpromising, with cliffs nearly down to the water, he thought that enough rock and soil could be blasted away to provide space for a single railtrack to a second, smaller wharf, for moorings and storage.

'As for the c-condition of the harbour itself, why you can smell it even through the ice!' declared Donald. 'Everything finds its way there, from sewage to severed legs. The army blames the hurricane of 14th November, but in my opinion it's the result of months of criminal neglect. Every day, bloated corpses of animals and men are towed out to sea but it never gets cleared properly. It's a wonder to me there's anyone still alive in the town, apart from the vultures.

'Everyone still talks about the hurricane as though it only happened yesterday—how tents, stores and carts were blown hundreds of yards by the gale; how the steamer *Prince*, filled with winter clothing and blankets for the troops, was dashed to pieces against the cliffs whilst at anchor outside the harbour; how the big drum of the Fourth Foot was one of many that bounded down the hill straight into the harbour—and so on.

'Lord Raglan's all right, of course, and, I must admit, was very civil to me when I called on him after my arrival,' said Donald, pointing to another sketchmap of the peninsula. 'His ADCs established a snug HQ for him in a Russian farmhouse, complete with stables and outbuildings which accommodated the staff as well, plus support troops. But, for divisions in the line it's been pure hell.' There they were, 660 feet up on the Chersonese plateau, completely dependent for supplies on one rough track winding up from Balaklava. Army engineers had commandeered every ammunition mule and baggage horse they could lay hands on, the only other transport available being light bullock carts and country arabas, which quickly disintegrated. If it hadn't been for help from some naval captains like Lushington and Peel in providing parties of willing sailors, probably no guns at all would have been dragged up into position.

'Then after the hurricane came the rain which swept away all tracks and obliterated the plain with the vilest mud, feet deep. That's still the story today.'

'Well,' I asked Donald, 'where do we go from the harbour?'

'As straight as an arrow, at the start—right up the main street of the town. It's the quickest route out to Kadikoi across the plain. We'll be able to knock down most of the old buildings and shacks and incidentally rid the place of those pestilential Turks; also the stones and rubble will make good hard-core for the rail bed. Then it's one and a half miles on the level, though the ground is boggy, and we'll have to bridge or dam rivulets by the score. Luckily, I've found a large bed of tolerable ballast outside Kadikoi, ideal for consolidation.'

By now the saloon was quite dark, but with the aid of an oil lamp and one of Stone's clear drawings, Donald took us quickly through the last stages of his proposed route. 'Outside Kadikoi,' he said, 'it will turn sharply to the west, skirt the foot of the hill by the Sailors' four-gun battery and pass through the French camp.

'Then comes a tricky stage,' he went on, 'finding the best route up Frenchman's Hill, where General Vinoy has his HQ, and on to the Flagstaff at the top of the plateau. I actually surveyed two routes, and plumped for one up the north-eastern side where the original track ran. I've based all my calculations on that route.'

'What about the gradients?' I asked.

'Steep, but just acceptable,' he replied. 'Thank God we've brought stationary engines or we'd never get our lumbering steep-sided wagons up the slope.'

After reaching the top the going was fairly straightforward, he judged, swinging north and following the surface between the Second and Light Divisions to the Woronzoff Road. Only a few small sandstone cuttings would be required. There would also be a branch to the west, serving the Third and Fourth Divisions, the siege train and the Commissariat.

Donald put down his notes while Stone carefully rolled up the maps. One look at his determined face told everything about the tremendous effort he had made to drive the survey thus so far. 'You and your lads have done a great job,' I said, clapping him warmly on the back. Stone grinned quietly, a tiny figure still thawing out in his heavy sweaters. A steward brought us welcome mugs of hot toddy.

'Obviously it's single track, to begin with,' I said, 'but I want to start double-track running between Balaklava and Kadikoi as soon as the railway opens.'

'Here's to the survey!' I exclaimed, raising my mug. 'We'll walk your route tomorrow, Donald, from end to end. We've got to be crystal clear about every detail before I put the scheme to the Board of Officers, let alone tackle Lord Raglan for help with labour.'

The hot toddy went down a treat. 'You'll be seeing parts of the front line his Lordship hasn't even inspected once,' said Donald, chuckling. 'I'll bring horses for you and Henry tomorrow morning early, otherwise we'll never cover the distance in one day.'

As I went up to the deck with them both I suddenly felt the menace of the bitter wind. 'Easier for the animals if it stays cold,' said Donald. 'Snow gives at least them a foothold. But I wouldn't put it past this climate for a thaw to set in overnight!'

8

NIGHTMARE JOURNEYS

19ᵗʰ January

It was one thing to say, in the warmth of the saloon and the glow of Donald's stirring achievement, that we would 'walk the whole route tomorrow.' It was quite another to contemplate the prospect as we awoke at dawn. Everything in the cabin felt damp and cheerless. Even Henry had little to say beyond a grunt as we huddled into our thickest clothing and pulled on thigh-length boots. The saloon portholes were all steamed up, so we concentrated on putting away platefuls of bacon and fried bread, praying the rum in the tea would set our blood tingling.

I climbed the ladder to the main deck, bracing myself for the inevitable icy blast, then stood there open-mouthed. Exactly as Donald had jokingly predicted, a thaw *had* set in; the wind was now blowing from the south-east and I could smell the harbour in its full pungency. Over the ship's side there was no trace of water; the whole surface was covered with a thick greenish-black scum from which protruded rotting carcasses of bullocks and mules—even the hind-legs of a camel—water-logged boxes, bales of hay, rotting food and waste of all kinds. Most shocking was the upper part of a soldier's corpse, still clad in a tattered tunic. Everywhere, on splintered balks of timber, vultures were perching precariously, their long red necks extended as they tore at the rank flesh bobbing on the surface.

Donald and Jack Wright were waiting on the rough quayside holding the horses for our journey. We slithered down the gangway and picked our way gingerly over to them between ragged potholes overflowing with slush and refuse. Our horses were little more than half-grown ponies, pitifully thin and ill-shod, with saddles hard as boards and bridles cobbled together with bits of rope.

'Not as s-smart as the Curragh,' said Donald with his great laugh, 'but they know the ground.' He led the way off the wharf across what looked like the remains of a garden run to seed. This when cleared would make a reasonable marshalling yard, he said. Behind it stood a building now used as the Army Post Office. Before the war it had been a neat whitewashed house with a wooden balcony and rooms on an upper floor, reached by an outside staircase. Only the main shape of the house now remained, much the worse for wear and standing in a sea of mud.

In contrast to yesterday the whole waterfront was now alive. Sailors were sweeping slush overboard, drenched by streams of melting snow from yards and rigging. Peddlers and traders were urging tiny mules loaded with panniers towards the anchored ships. Beggars appeared from nowhere searching for scraps on the newly-exposed ground, Small detachments of soldiers were filling potholes with stones.

The track we took ran along beside one wooden building larger and more strongly constructed than its fellows. Its front door was double-padlocked, but a long line of ragged soldiers was forming outside. Donald shouted over his shoulder: 'The Commissary-General's staff don't open up until 8 am and they shut the store on the dot of 5.30 pm. The soldiers on ration-duty get here early because it's easier to walk on the track when it's frozen solid. They'll have a tough journey back today, poor sods.' The men, pinched and silent, hardly glanced up as we passed by. It took half an hour to thread a way through Balaklava's main street where sullen Turks, Greeks, Armenians and Egyptian traders were getting up stalls and unloading merchandise from primitive hand carts. 'They'll be gone soon, thank God,' shouted Donald cheerfully above the hubbub. Most of the houses looked old and tumbledown; there were even cannonballs lying in the roadway, relics of the battle for Balaklava.

Once clear I got my first uninterrupted view of the terrain. Northwards some two miles across the plain lay the small village of Kadikoi. On all the high peaks around snow was still lying in great sheets, dazzling the eye as a sudden shaft of sun caught the slanting surfaces. The silence was broken only by the sound of rifle fire from the front lines and the nearer whirring flight of widgeon, teal and wild duck. I couldn't wait to get my shotgun out from England!

Every foot of the way forward showed very clearly the practical problems that Donald had highlighted; the plain's whole surface was criss-crossed by scores of rivulets, many merging into formidable streams which would make track-laying tricky: Donald had done well to unearth an accessible bed of ballast. Though our horses picked their way carefully, mud was up to their fetlocks, making every movement exhausting. We often dismounted to plod along beside them.

Down the track from Kadikoi an irregular string of small black shapes was inching forward. As we approached the leading group, Donald halted and we pulled aside. What passed silently was a vision straight from hell: three emaciated mules, each led by a driver muffled in rags, to whose saddles were tied sick, wavering figures, hands roughly bandaged against frostbite with a pallor as of death on their faces. These were the vanguard of a straggling procession on their way to the hospital ships at Balaklava, for transfer thence—if they survived—to Scutari. A bullock-drawn araba bore a rigid figure, his left leg amputated at the thigh, and with only a blanket flung over for cover. Jolting past us, he stuffed a corner of it into his mouth to stifle a cry.

Stopping frequently to consider bridging requirements, we were passed by a silent, seemingly never-ending line of soldiers dressed in bread-bags trudging wearily towards the Commissariat stores for rations. One or two mounted officers were bent on a similar pursuit, to buy food from the sutlers' stalls or provisions and the occasional luxury from authorised stores held on HMS *Derbyshire*, sold at strictly controlled prices. Even more surprising was the number of officers on foot, some clad in rabbit skins, scarcely distinguishable from that of the fusiliers—no gold lace, not even colour left in jackets which were patched and stained. Strips of towel protected the ends of trousers: mufflers and motley caps topped the outfits. On every face was a uniform blankness, eyes were directed down towards the treacherous ground where a stumble could mean a broken leg.

We had always intended to establish a mid-point depot to relieve pressure on our main storage yards at Balaklava. Donald showed us a level stretch he had selected to the west of Kadikoi. It was right beside our intended route, and I immediately agreed it. After a mouthful or two of cold meat and a tot of rum, we pressed on, anxious at the complex cloud patterns developing above the Sapoune Heights to our left. The wind was, however, still southerly with a thaw increasing by the minute. Layers of our discarded clothing were hung on the necks of our patient, plodding beasts. A tough trek lay ahead. It was already 9.30 am.

We passed the RA camp and the Sailors' battery at the foot of Frenchman's Hill and saw, to the north, vineyards and ravines stretching away, and in the distance the metalled Woronzoff Road— enemy territory. Donald had chosen to follow the old track on the north-eastern side of the Hill, at the top of which General Vinoy had his HQ. 'I worried whether I had made the best choice,' said Donald quietly, 'but the gradients on the west side are really fierce.' I thought he had achieved a very creditable one-in-seven, considering that gradients on the old track beside his route were twice as steep in places. 'Our stationary engines are brand-new,' I said with a grin. 'They'll cope.'

It was slogging work on foot up the half-mile slope, leading our tired horses through slush and thickening mud. And this was only January, I kept reminding myself. February, by all accounts, was always a more difficult month; while March was being predicted as worse still. All I could think of was our desperate need for speed— and still greater speed. Every day gained by our labours would, DV, mean one day less of misery for our wracked soldiers.

The Col of Balaklava was reached around mid-day, a place swept bare of all landmarks by torrents of slush and loosened boulders. While the horses munched hay there we finished the rest of the meat. 'Rum's the s-stuff at times like this,' remarked Donald, the world's most philosophical campaigner. I could just make out Lord Raglan's HQ through the mist about half a mile to the north-west—a fair-sized farmhouse from whose chimneys pale blue smoke was being blown about the sky. Around it was a sprawl of huts and tents. It could wait for closer inspection until the next afternoon, I decided, when I had presented our plan to the Board of Officers. My prime task now was to estimate every hazard of our line to the yard, and remember what I had seen.

We struck north across the relatively level surface of the plateau which made horse transport possible again. As we rode through the lines of General Bosquet's two French divisions, Donald recounted a rumour that Lord Raglan was actually contemplating an early visit to Balaklava, stung by adverse comments from officers and men and reported by Russell in his *Times* dispatches of the C-in-C's 'non-appearance' among his troops.

At the Forks, Donald had suggested, our line should diverge, the left-hand branch striking almost due west to end at a Commissariat dump serving Sir Richard England's Second Division and also the Fourth Division. Nearby in the Old Fort the latter division's late commander, General Cathcart, lay buried along with General Strange-ways and Collis and several other officers. The other branch would run slightly north-east to a second dump serving the Second Division, Sir George Brown's Light Division, the first Division, commanded by the Duke of Cambridge, and the siege train.

Gunfire was being exchanged steadily but it didn't appear to threaten us directly, and I made to go forward to glimpse our front lines and outlying piquets; I was halted by Donald's shout: 'Look left, Jim.' He was pointing upwards to the west where dark sullen clouds had made a sudden reappearance. As I watched, the whole sky began to turn steel-grey, and the wind increased in force, now coming from the north. The noise of shells and rifle fire was louder and more menacing; flurries of snow fell on our exposed faces and on the mufflers and oilskins we had cast on our ponies' necks.

'We've got to be quick if we're to make it back before nightfall,' said Donald, urgently. We set off at once—a nightmare descent against the clock—half slide, half plod right down from the Col with our horses slithering at our heels. Along the way we encountered returning ration-laden parties and equally bowed officers, struggling upwards with their provisions and bundles of firewood strapped on their backs.

At last, in whirling snow we reached the quayside and saw *Sprite*'s welcoming lights dully reflected in the stinking waters.

'You two have done a magnificent job,' I told Donald and

Wright. 'We've ample material now to convince any Board of Officers, however cantankerous. You, Stone, make several copies of the route—bold and convincing—with a special one for Lord Raglan. I'll show it to him tomorrow afternoon.' Silently, they both turned, leading the steaming horses away. Henry and I went up the gangplank and stumbled down to our cabin, painfully shifting one mud-clogged boot past the other. Henry poured each of us a stiff glass of rum. Minutes later we began the long job of stripping off sodden clothing. Henry fell into his bunk: he'd proved a solid companion that day. I sat on, fixing clear in my mind an exact picture of what we had seen: the chaos, the perils of the army's position, the menace offered by the land and weather. And it was still only mid-January...

I pushed such thoughts aside to make notes of salient points, deeply grateful to have such a colleague as Donald. Though his glasses might get steamed up he was a fighter through and through—a true professional. With his help I could fulfil Mr. Peto's promise to the Prime Minister. Comforted, I soon followed Henry into a dreamless sleep.

9

CONFRONTATIONS

20th January

I wakened early, stiff in every limb and with the reek of sodden clothing in my nostrils. Snow on the porthole dimmed the thin dawn light, but my head felt clear. I got up, leaving Henry asleep, threw on a reefer coat, pulled on fresh socks and boots and went thankfully along to the saloon. Anywhere smelt better than that cabin. Also I was determined to write a good letter to Sarah before getting engulfed in the day's business.

A steward brought a mug of tea and the news, which I felt already in my bones, that it was still snowing and blowing hard from the north. I re-read my diary entries since my arrival, and wrote to Sal:

> *Balaklava*
> *25th January*
>
> *It is utterly impossible for even the most graphic pen to describe this place. Picture the dirtiest village in all Ireland and add in imagination about 6 inches more dirt and filth: that will enable you to form some notion. There are just one-third enough men here— fancy half the army being employed in carrying up provisions and huts for the other half.*
>
> *The cavalry horses have been reduced to skeletons, unable to carry the men; the horse artillery is little better, and the police force (in which was young Watkins) has dwindled to 12 out of 30 or thereabouts. Watkins has gone home ill; the remainder are either dead or in hospital. There is*

*everything to eat here except the most essential—one
can get potted meats and such luxuries, but not a
pound of hay to feed the starving horses.*

*Thinking of the suffering of the men causes me to
feel that every day wasted makes me in a sort of way
an accessory to their privations. If it pleases God to
spare my health I shall be quite content, and if
nothing else I hope to get home again to you with the
happy feeling of having done my best to benefit my
fellow men.*

Your most affectionate and attached husband.

At that point my mind filled with the memory of those soldiers I
saw yesterday being brought painfully and silently down from the
plateau. The previous week over 1,000 men had apparently been
taken off to Scutari, and three more ships were due away over the next
few days. Every day more dying, every day more dead!

In a fury of anger I turned my attention to the forthcoming
meeting: what if the Board of Officers should raise absurd objections;
what if they attempted to veto my proposals? I remembered Lord
Stratford's parting advice: 'Stick to your plan; deliver your railway as
promised—that will silence the critics.' After tramping over Donald's
survey route yesterday I felt quietly confident we could achieve our
aim. But seven miles in seven weeks...?

I vowed it would take more than an ad hoc Board to stop me. I
would confront Lord Raglan that very afternoon with a demand for
assistance from any quarter—troops, labourers, any available
bodies—to help clear the port area as a base for our operations.

Suddenly there were loud voices from the deck, and heavy steps
down the stairway. Campbell burst in, with Stone following. 'The
Board is playing silly-b-buggers,' he shouted, 'Captain Heath has just
told me that we're only third on the agenda for the meeting. Th-third,
I ask you!'

'Who's on it this morning?' I asked.

'A ragbag and bobtail lot,' replied Donald, flinging himself down
at the table and unloosing his oilskins. 'The president is a Major

Hargreaves, RE. The top man, Sir John Burgoyne, couldn't even be bothered to come down from headquarters. There are a couple of admin officers, and a Captain Parks from the 39th Foot, just disembarked. Captain Heath'll be there too: the meeting's aboard his ship. I reckon we'll be lucky to be called before 11 am.'

He passed me the drawings Stone had made overnight. Each was finished with meticulous accuracy, as thoroughly executed as in a contractor's drawing office in England. Donald's route stood out from the page boldly in Indian ink, with blocks of red and pale blue to indicate Allied units and buildings, including Lord Raglan's HQ on the plateau and our forward dispositions of troops and artillery.

'Th-this is what will really interest them,' observed Donald, pointing to the map of our proposed harbour layout. 'They can see what we're planning by simply squinting out of the portholes. I followed Captain Heath's suggestion about keeping our track back from the quayside—that'll please him. As for the other officers…'

'It will just have to please them whatever their objections,' I replied. 'I'm changing nothing. It's these plans Lord Raglan will see this afternoon.'

I turned to Henry who had just come into the cabin. 'After breakfast, will you get a couple of the strongest horses you can find for Donald and me—and hay, as well. It's going to be a rough ride.'

Sprite's cook did us proud for breakfast—an egg apiece, and marmalade. Donald looked like a biblical patriarch with his vast beard, but I determined to stay clean-shaven for that day—a decision I regretted minutes later while trying to scrape off stubble in cold water. I dressed as neatly as possible, a bit ashamed of the state of my boots, but they wouldn't show anyway as the snow was already inches deep.

Long before the start of our meeting, Donald and I were on the quarter-deck of HMS *Sanspareil* being greeted by the robust, black-bearded figure of Captain Heath. 'Delighted to welcome you, Mr. Beatty,' he boomed, 'and Mr. Campbell—again. I gather you've been over the ground.'

'Yes,' I replied, 'there's no time to lose; we've settled our route. I feel I should represent to you, sir, that our business should have headed the agenda this morning.'

'Quite so, but it is not in my power to command the order in which the Board of Officers conducts its affairs. I attend only as Admiral of the Port, representing the navy's interests. I'm sure you'll find the officers as keen as you to speed progress. Unfortunately, two other matters have been given precedence over your project.'

From his apologetic tone it was clear where his sympathies lay; had he been in charge of proceedings he would have brooked delay no more than he would have countenanced the minutest blemish on his quarter-deck. As he led us below, I glimpsed the backs of the four officers of that morning's Board filing into the Captain's cabin: they did not appear to be hurrying unduly.

Our turn came eventually, by which time I was near spitting. What struck me at once was the atmosphere which greeted us—with one exception it was hostile and indifferent—much in keeping with the cold, frosty air of the cabin. I studied the faces in front of me with care. The president, a thin, sallow major, rose to his feet. 'Hargreaves, Royal Engineers,' he announced. 'Permit me to introduce my colleagues—Colonel Sterling, Captain Popplewell, Captain Park, 39th Foot. You already know Captain Heath, I see. The Board has much business ahead of us; I trust we can deal with this matter of your railway quickly.'

The remark was stinging. 'As quickly as possible,' I retorted. 'I must stress that this matter of *our* railway, as you term it, is now very much exercising the minds of both the Prime Minister and the Secretary of State for War who have authorised me to mount this expedition, and I must register my astonishment at the absence of Sir John Burgoyne from this discussion.'

My remark clearly discomforted the Board. 'Sir John,' said Major Hargreaves, looking as though he had bitten on a chilli, but in a more conciliatory tone, 'is in conference with the Field Marshal and the French generals: he has nominated me to represent him.' He gave a slight bow; the others' faces were expressionless, save for a flicker of amusement on Captain Park's lips. My heart warmed to him. I passed Stone's drawings round the table, curious to see their reactions. The president sifted through two or three sheets in a perfunctory manner (it was difficult to believe that he was RE and not just some jumped-up regimental engineer out of his depth); Captain Popplewell hardly glanced at the plans (for him obviously the whole issue was solely our affair—a typical admin reaction); Captain Park applied himself to the drawings with genuine enthusiasm. Colonel Sterling, seated directly opposite me, was another matter entirely. His whole body was rigid with disapproval. He looked what he was, a battle-hardened professional, and brigade-major of the 71st, to boot. His manner made plain that in his time he had seen many plans hailed as brilliant, only to watch them founder: he had drawn up many schemes himself, no question. 'I must tell you at the outset, Mr. Beatty,' he stated with a cold glare, 'the principal want of our army is a regularly-organised baggage-train.'

I chose to ignore the remark at this stage, anxious to put the full sweep of our proposals forward first. It seemed by now that I was covering almost familiar ground, and memory helped fill in main details of the weight and scope of the enterprise—and most tellingly, I thought, our all-out construction timetable. At that point I noticed Major Hargreaves glance towards the cabin portholes. It was doubtless still snowing heavily outside.

As I passed the large-scale harbour drawings round I caught a keen look in Captain Heath's eyes, and asked Donald to take over. With no trace of a stammer, no misting up of glasses, his presentation was solid and impressive: 'I took particular note of the Captain's suggestion about the siting of the line along the quays,' he said, 'and as you see I have moved it back so that large vessels can lay their anchors safely across the beach road. I have also adopted his proposal to use the next street for our main track out of Balaklava, with sidings to our yard. For the moment we'll unload at the Ordnance Wharf— it's the only one big enough—but our plan is to have a new railway wharf alongside as fast as we can build it.'

'I can't agree to the Ordnance Wharf being commandeered like that,' said Major Hargreaves.

'I concur,' agreed Colonel Sterling.

'But it's the only feasible place that's big enough at the moment,' I said. 'We must have it for our first two ships.' I made it quite clear I would make a major issue of this point if they persisted.

The tension was finally broken by the Captain. 'I'm very taken with the route you propose: I'm sure it's the best through the town.' Then he looked at us candidly. 'But I must in all honesty say, gentlemen, I doubt your capacity to have a railway in action within three weeks of your force arriving: I'd prefer one thousand mules arriving *today*.'

However, he and the other officers cheered up when Donald explained our intention of providing an entirely new wharf on the western side of the harbour, to be served by a single line. 'Capital,' he exclaimed. 'When can I have it?'

After a long pause, the president asked: 'Any immediate problems, Mr. Beatty?' I told him of Lord Stratford's attempt to recruit labourers for initial work, and of the men's refusal to come. I needed two hundred soldiers and draught animals now until our navvy ships arrived. At that there was an even longer silence.

'Don't you understand our position, Mr. Beatty?' exclaimed Major Hargreaves. 'There *is* no surplus manpower available. From what I can make of your plan a railway seems feasible, but I have doubts about the capacity of winding engines to pull loaded wagons up a one-in-seven gradient. Indeed, will there be enough water from wells on the plateau for stationary engines and other purposes?'

Colonel Sterling wasted no time. 'You say, Mr. Beatty, you must have men and animals. I have listened carefully to your whole proposal, but I heard no mention of locomotives. All you appear to be bringing are wagons weighing fourteen tons to be drawn along your tram-road by our miserable ponies.'

'We'll have our own horses,' I explained, but there was no way of calming him down.

'I protest,' he said vehemently, 'even if I'm the only protester, at this monstrous notion of using our soldiers in this way. Your tramway, Mr. Beatty, entails making a road between the rails—and one available only for railway wagons and horses. A good ordinary macadamised road could be used by every kind of cart, and by mules and troops.'

That was the colonel's final word. I glanced at the administrative officer, Captain Popplewell. With a weary shrug he supported his senior. Only Captain Park responded positively. 'I bet 39th Foot can manage something, Mr. Beatty,' he said. 'I know we've only just disembarked and are busy setting up camp, but I'll tackle my CO at once.'

'The navy's always good for a few sailors,' added Captain Heath. 'Nothing appeals to a tar more than tackling the impossible. You have my vote, Mr. Beatty, though I could still do with one thousand mules in the meantime.'

After more argument the Board reached a reluctant, face-saving consensus: the route would be approved, in principle. I instantly got up: 'I shall report this to the Field Marshal this afternoon. Good-day, gentlemen; thank you.'

Donald and I were quickly back on shore, our feet breaking through the thin crust on the drifting snow. Henry appeared, leading two tolerably strong-looking nags. 'Bought them from a sailor off *Volcano*,' he announced with amazement. 'Cheap, really, at twenty pounds apiece, but I've no idea where they came from.'

Once saddled and with fresh oilskins, Donald and I made off north, smack into thickly falling snow. Past Kadikoi we walked our mounts laboriously up Frenchman's Hill to the top of the plateau. Ration parties bound for Balaklava constantly passed; then a small convoy of desperately struggling wounded. Donald told me of a message he had seen from one general ordering his subalterns to wear swords, to distinguish them from the men. I couldn't help wondering what he would have made of one officer I saw who slouched past us, clad in red Russian boots up to his middle, a white skin coat embroidered down the back with flowers and a leather cap topped with a London dustman's hood. From his serious face he could have been pondering on matters of high policy; probably he was merely working out his chances of buying a pot of jam from a purser: butter was out of the question; it was available only in casks; as for moving the huge boxes and scores of army hut sections lying on the Balaklava beach, they were far too heavy for men to transport. We alone would be able to accomplish that—but how soon?

To the north I could see a few Russian carts stealing from Mackenzie's Farm towards the heights of Inkerman, while along the

Tchernaya valley several Cossack piquets were riding about. One could envy those ruffians who might only have iron-tipped wooden lances and ragged ponies but yet were clad in sheepskin coats and fur hats. The British cavalry simply were not able to face such conditions.

Cannonades of both sides went echoing round the mountains. Sharpshooters were persistent as woodpeckers, and flights of geese and curlews filled the sky with their plaintive cries as they sought in vain for once-familiar landing places.

Less than three hours of daylight were left. Re-mounted, we followed a better-kept track to Lord Raglan's headquarters at the head of a ravine running down to Dockyard Creek. Outside his farmhouse a Union Jack fluttered from its flagpole in the snow flurries. The wind, mercifully, was easing slightly. Round an outer compound was a huddle of nondescript one-storey buildings, interspersed with tents of varying sizes, for junior staff officers and Hussars of the guard.

Our way was barred by a sentry who made us wait outside while the Military Secretary was informed. Soon Colonel Steele appeared with a cordial enough greeting, particularly to Donald whom he had met earlier. He took us to an office in the main building, saying we had chosen an unfortunate day. Lord Raglan was in council with General Canrobert, his opposite number, and General Bosquet. 'They may well have to remain for the night,' he added. 'You can see the French HQ, to the east across the ravine. His Lordship knew of your departure from Constantinople and was looking forward to meeting you. However, I hope I may be of assistance.'

I came to the point. 'The Board of Officers has this morning approved the route for the railway which Mr. Campbell has surveyed. I have come to request immediate military help in preparing our wharf area in Balaklava before the arrival of our first ships with men and materials.'

'When do you expect them?'

'At the end of this month. If we can start the clearing work now, it will save precious time and we'll be that much sooner getting the line into action. "Seven miles in seven weeks" was Mr. Peto's pledge to the Prime Minister, you know!'

Colonel Steele looked coldly at me. 'No doubt Major Hargreaves informed you of our manpower problem?' I nodded. 'It hasn't changed since this morning,' he said bluntly. 'But aren't problems there to be overcome?' I protested. 'Captain Park, who was also on the Board, promised to speak to his commanding officer—39th Foot—about lending some men.'

'Ah, yes, the 39th. Perhaps something might be arranged there. It will take time, I'm afraid.'

I drew a letter from my pocket. 'I have ventured to write directly to His Lordship, setting out our minimum needs. May I ask you, sir, to be so kind as to put it in his hands at the earliest moment, with these explanatory maps?'

Colonel Steele opened my letter, scanned its contents and glanced at the maps. 'I promise you, Mr. Beatty, Lord Raglan shall have all this today. He and I are both anxious for your success. It is just that...' Here he broke off, perhaps regretting the phrase he was about to finish, and asked hurriedly whether we would like something to eat. As the council was clearly in full swing next door I declined, but before leaving I again expressed my astonishment that no senior Royal Engineer officer had presided over the Board's deliberations. 'I understand Colonel Burgoyne's absence, but surely he has a second-in-command?'

'Colonel Stanton is sick, and has already gone down to Balaklava for passage to England.'

I suppose I might have mentioned Burgoyne's two ADCs, Burke and Stopford, but would they, I wondered, have been any more effectual than Major Hargreaves? By this time I had had enough of prevarication. As we prepared to go, Colonel Steele said politely he hoped that on our next visit we would at least stay overnight. On our way to the gate an orderly thrust packets of sandwiches into our hands and a flask of rum. 'This snow'll make it a bugger of a ride down, sir,' he said cheerfully.

Our horses, which I was glad to note had been stabled and fed, stepped out gamely into a bleak landscape. Snow was already obliterating the path and they were soon stumbling in hidden potholes. In single file we walked the animals down the painful gradient to the Sailors' Battery, Donald patiently checking out the treacherous surface. Even through the snow, the stench of dead horses and mules that had slithered off this track into the gullies was nauseating. Much more unnerving were the occasional despairing neighs and sudden leg movements of animals unlucky enough to be still alive after their falls.

Men, how was I to get men? How to break through this infernal military red tape? Where to turn? Then I remembered Donald mentioning a sympathetic officer he had come across some days earlier near Kadikoi—Sir Colin Campbell, commander of the Highland Brigade, a man who, he declared, believed in the potential of a railway. I determined to seek his aid; at the most I would bombard the Navy through Captain Heath. I would write privately to Lord Stratford about the position.

It was pitch black and still snowing remorselessly as we finally fetched up exhausted at *Sprite*. Henry did his best to help restore us to our senses. He found dry clothes and sat us at the saloon table facing bowls of steaming soup. We ate our way solidly through tinned ham and potatoes, rounding off with cheese and mugs of coffee hot enough to burn one's ears off, while he gave us his news.

'Captain Heath thinks he can make more space available to us for harbour storage. Tomorrow he's asking two Naval Brigade officers for immediate volunteers. He thinks he may be able to get us quarters ashore. 'The snow has stopped,' he added. Donald, nodding good-night, remarked: 'It'll be gone by morning.'

Henry was turning into a very useful lad. I must tell Sarah, I thought, sleepily picking up the letter I had started so early that morning. There was nothing I could add to it: even my handwriting stumbled with tiredness. The prospect of a place of our own ashore glowed like a beacon. *Press forward* was the last thing that flashed across my mind before I fell asleep, absolutely done.

10

NEW FACES—NEW PROBLEMS

21st January

After yesterday's buffeting my face felt too sore for shaving; I decided to grow a beard like Donald and everyone else here, except Sir George Brown, commander of the First Division. He was one of the old school, reputedly the best-dressed man in the army, adamant that the rank and file should wear leather stocks summer and winter alike.

Today, a day of surprises. Setting off urgently to contact Sir Colin Campbell, I found a changed world as I stepped on deck. A thaw had set in! The wind had backed right round, the lowering clouds were shifting northwards and there was a glint of blue in the sky. I dodged the showers of melting snow from the spars and stepped on to the brimming wharf. Donald was running towards me. 'Get Henry out at once,' he shouted. '*Arabia*'s on fire, three ships down: she's a powder vessel.' We watched flames shooting up through cargo hatches blown apart by the pressure inside the hull. Sparks and fragments of glowing wood were spraying everywhere and black smoke rolled up the harbour. 'Who'd have believed it?' remarked Donald. 'Only a fortnight ago, *Star of the North* berthed here with a thousand tons of powder and ammunition on board; next day, fire broke out in her lower hold, six feet from the magazine. They just got it out in time. Now it's *Arabia*'s turn next door, and further along are two more powder ships, *Medora* and *Earl of Shaftesbury*!'

'The sooner we get our western wharf built the better,' I said, 'If anything goes wrong now, all Balaklava will be blown sky high.'

Arabia's sailors were pumping furiously, helped by a hose from the steamer *Niagara*: hundreds of gallons of water went flooding down below; the billows of smoke began to thin.

I could see anxious officers on the three hospital ships at double anchor near the harbour entrance with steam up. They were due out soon for Scutari, each carrying 1,000 patients, and obviously debating whether to shift out now for safety. Lighters crammed with wounded men were rowing frantically towards the last vessel. Across the water I could hear the shouts of agony as patient after patient was hauled roughly aboard. Some might prefer death by explosion as an option. I determined to provide a spur to our terminus layout so that wagons could run sick men right down to the quayside. Already within past weeks 8,000 men had been shipped out to Scutari or back to England.

'Look,' said Donald, pointing along the quay, 'there's Adjutant-General Estcourt. I heard he was coming down from HQ this morning to inspect the town and welcome the new superintendent, Colonel Harding. Let's hope he is better than his predecessor, who was useless.'

The flames of *Arabia* died down. I told Donald I intended to meet both General Campbell and Commissary-General Filder that morning and to get our quarters ashore settled. 'I'll be happy to come with you to see Sir Colin,' he said. 'We've been on good terms since I arrived. But that Mr. Filder now, he's quite another s-story. You'll have to work your own magic by yourself there. He won't listen to anyone's second-in-command, that man. Dug out of the bogs of Ireland—if you'll excuse the phrase—at the age of sixty-eight for this job of all jobs. Admitted, he did good work in the Peninsula, I'm told. But not an atom of feeling: he's a walking book of regulations. If Satan himself signed a requisition it would have to be counter-signed by God! He makes me s-sick, makes everyone sick at heart who deals with him.' A long speech from Donald, with many a revealing stammer.

'Well, we *have* to deal with him, otherwise we don't exist officially.'

'That's why you're the boss, Jim,' he replied simply. 'Sir Colin can be just as hard as Filder, but he's a gentleman, and he does listen and connect with facts most of the time.'

I asked Donald why the town commandant hadn't been at the Board meeting, especially as we intended to change his whole area out of recognition. The answer was that he had already left Balaklava to rejoin his regiment and that Colonel Harding had only taken up his new appointment that very morning. A poor reason, I considered; maybe he simply hadn't appreciated the significance of the matter to be discussed.

We might all too rarely get at facts but we were inundated with hourly rumours—one that Lord Raglan himself would be coming in a day or two for a conference with Admiral Sir Edmund Lyons on HMS *Caradoc*. I wondered whether I might be able to nobble him then. When I glanced past the flagship towards the northern edge of the harbour, the swampy beach there was littered with dying bullocks and the endless corpses of mules black with flies. The 39th Foot, setting up camp nearby, had my sympathy. They were right beside the stream that carried down waste from the field hospitals together with nameless army swill.

The thaw brought with it the full unpleasantness of the harbour's odours. They reminded me suddenly of those that used to waft up from the abattoir at the bottom of our tiny street in Enniskillen—Pudding Lane—where we lived in my boyhood: a memory long forgotten but triggered now by a familiar age-old smell!

The Commissariat department stood solid behind the desolate stretch where our sidings and storage sheds would be rising. Its roof looked hurricane-proof; each of the many windows gleamed with unbroken glass. Inside, stoves were at full blast. A surprised clerk informed me that Commissary-General Filder was indeed free to speak to me. I pushed behind a tall screen and found him half hidden behind a file-stacked table, looking for all the world like a marksman behind a parapet. Two pale blue eyes registered unwinkingly on my face; he was a small man, wiry, immobile.

As I stepped forward, he extended a hard, dry hand. 'Mr. Beatty, good morning. I have heard of you, as doubtless you have of me.' His thin voice still held a trace of the Irish lilt of his youth, though a lifetime of controlling the food, clothing and pay of armies in the field had smothered any softness under an authoritarian tone. This was the man who had served under the then Sir Charles Wellesley throughout the Peninsular War. Now sixty-eight—or was it seventy-four?—he had been recalled from retirement. He and his henchmen held total sway: one could see as much in every line of that inflexible face. 'I hope to become better acquainted with you, sir,' I replied politely. 'We shall be having much to do with each other in the coming months.'

'So I am informed,' he said sharply. 'You and your men are set to bring a lot of problems.'

'On the contrary,' I informed him: 'I expect us to provide solutions, and be of service to your operations very shortly. Meanwhile, we plan to be as self-sufficient as possible.'

His response was coldly insulting: 'All I require in the way of help from your Civil Engineering Corps, Mr. Beatty, is a correct tally of numbers each week so I can balance my pay accounts. Now, if you will excuse me, I'm extremely occupied. Please deal in future through my chief writer. Good day to you.' My planned offer of assistance in transporting all the army's stores by rail to the camps died in my throat.

I went out and looked through a rear window at that chief writer, a Mr. Juken, as it later turned out. He seemed an exact replica of his beady-eyed master: Commissary-General Filder was a shrewd picker of staff. I restrained an impulse to put a fist through one of his snug windows.

Donald stood in front of me, chuckling. 'You've been having the full Filder treatment, I see,' he observed, 'H-here's two bits of good news, though. Captain Heath tells me that Captain Lushington has promised to cough up two hundred Jacks as soon as he's got rosters settled, and he's now off to tackle Captain Peel of HMS *Diamond* for men. Another gent! And, guess what, a friend has just put me on to possible quarters for us in the town. The owner has left—he died of typhus, actually. The house is being fumigated now. It's that or nothing, I'm afraid.'

'Great news, Donald,' I said. 'I'll have it. Let's take a look on our way to Sir Colin Campbell.'

The last hospital ship was slowly drawing out of the harbour as we left for the Highland camp. How many of its passengers would see Balaklava again? How many of my father's cholera patients ever made it back to their small farms?

95

Henry joined us, and we finally found the house—a two-storeyed affair—at the end of the town, just off the road to Kadikoi. Its late owner was a Turkish commander whose body had been taken, no doubt, to join the countless hundreds of his compatriots in their shallow graves stretching up the hills to the east. The walls and floors of the building were filthy, and there was little glass left in the windows. That was just as well since the place still stank of chloride of lime and gunpowder squibs which were the accepted local method of fumigation. However it would provide us with bedrooms and a communal sitting room upstairs, and with space for an office so that I could keep a check on progress. There was little furniture beyond bare essentials. I asked Henry to organise our immediate move and rustle up chairs and bedding. Donald cheerfully volunteered to join this strange new menage.

* * * * * * *

The scene before us was unbelievable: streams and rivulets across the sodden plain glistened in unexpected bursts of sunshine; everywhere water vapour was blowing away over stunted bushes and ragged grasses. After two hours of steady going—the last part uphill—we reached the tented headquarters of Highland Brigade. Several feet below the Rifles' position there was a clear view down the valley to the Tchernaya River. Under the eyes of NCOs, a wholesale spring-clean was taking place. Water had been boiled, canvas baths rigged up for the men—some were even scrubbing clothes. Boots, arms and equipment were being looked to by fusiliers, not in kilts but in breeks, blanket gaiters and mongrel leggings. Astride a barrel, a piper was playing a seemingly endless lament. It was the first music to strike my ears since I had landed in the Crimea. Donald told me that at Christmas the C-in-C had granted permission for regimental bands to play 'if the officers commanding saw fit'. Not one saw fit—not even a drum or bugle sounded in the camps. Long before then, calamity after calamity had struck the bands. At Inkerman the horse artillery had ridden across a large tent where the instruments of 88th Regiment were stored for safety. The final blow fell during the hurricane when

Fourth Regiment's big drum bounded down the hill and was smashed to pieces. Also the bandsmen were exhausted from unending stints as stretcher bearers. In the French camps it was very different: music was heard regularly throughout the darkest months.

Sir Colin Campbell's welcome was as warming as the brew he poured out for us—whisky (as they spell it in Scotland!). He and Donald were easy together, and I found myself included automatically in the camaraderie. 'Ye'll get nothing out of Lord Raglan's staff, laddie,' he remarked. 'They're the most useless set of officers I've encountered in a lifetime in the Queen's service—they're nearly all his nephews, of course. I doubt if they could organise you twenty men, let alone two hundred. I'd willingly lend you some of mine, but we have to watch the Cossacks like hawks night and day right now, and it will get worse as soon as the ground hardens again. When will your navvies be arriving?'

'In ten days, if they have a lucky passage.'

'And when can we expect the line to reach us here eh, laddie?'

'We'll get to Kadikoi by mid-February, Sir Colin,' I replied confidently. I had half-expected a sarcastic response from that canny Scots commander to a prophesy thus plucked out of thin air. In such manner can brave words be transformed into firm commitments!

'Excellent news.' he said. 'Good luck to you! We're relying on your railway for our hutting and ammunition—for everything.'

As we trotted slowly back, drowsy in the unexpectedly mild air, we made for 39th's camp. Captain Park was busy superintending the erection of a hut for the men—only the second to be put up since the regiment landed. They referred to themselves as 'the damned Dorsetshires', and seemed a rollicking, if somewhat reckless lot. Maybe it wasn't their fault; they'd been rushed out from Gibraltar without winter clothing or equipment, and had only been kitted properly out here courtesy of *The Times* benevolent fund.

Park ran across to us: 'My CO has agreed to lend one hundred men, maybe more once we've got ourselves established. The request's gone up to HQ. Two of our lieutenants have volunteered, as well. We'll start tomorrow.' I could hardly find words to thank him. 'I'll get our navvies cleaning up that poisonous beach just as soon as they arrive,' I vowed. 'Otherwise you'll all die of typhus.' Park thought that a rich joke.

Henry had done a great moving job to our new quarters, mightily helped by Wright and Stone; he'd even acquired a dining table and enough old chairs to put weary bottoms on. His pièce de resistance was two grimy faded curtains which he waved around like a victory banner. We slept there that night, oblivious to the stench of chlorine.

Balaklava
28th January 1855

My dearest Sarah,

I have read—and re-read—your first two letters with such joy and relief that you and the chicks are well. The fact that your second was written only on 3rd January is astonishing! Even more remarkable, that they have both reached me at all. Postal arrangements here are totally disorganised. I've not had a single newspaper; they're regarded as lawful plunder for the first comer. My new acquaintance Russell tells me that though forty copies of The Times *are sent to him daily he only gets about one a week. Donald hasn't heard once from his mother since he arrived in December, though he writes to her regularly.*

Both he and Henry are down at the harbour supervising our construction party of 'volunteers' from 39th Foot under Captain Park and two lieutenants. That's the first assistance we've had to date. My secret fear is that the regiment will be moved up to the plateau before they've completely finished preparing the site for our terminus. It's back-breaking work but they are really putting their hearts into it. Many are farm lads from Dorset, like their fathers before them but they're learning to wield shovels like navvies!

Our first ship should, DV, be arriving any day now: I pray God nothing goes astray. I long passionately for the track to be started: every day counts, especially in this changeable climate. Ironically, the last few days have been mild and dry: it's tantalising: I can't sleep for fretting though outwardly I hope I show myself as spirited as the rest.

Well, enough of moans. We've settled into a house in the town—primitive enough but a welcome change from our dark cabin on Sprite. *I'm writing in a ramshackle office dressed as though for outdoors, with the wind whistling straight through a broken window. Everything passes our front door—Croats, Bulgarians, all the swindlers of the Levant, as well as English and French soldiers and hosts of camp followers. My head is spinning with the endless racket of mules, camels and bullocks, and the creak of country carts lurching from one pothole to the next—and the curses of the drivers.*

Despite everything, we have good moments. Henry chatters non-stop, though since I made him Master of the Horse, he has taken his new responsibility very seriously. I felt bilious the other day and have found the box of medicines very handy: I've even been doctoring Donald with my blue pills. Now his route has been agreed, he's his old perky self again, stammering away like smoke and letting out great bursts of laughter, which set us all off.

Last night we had our first dinner party! I met your surgeon cousin Ethelbert Blake quite by chance on the quay. He has had a pretty severe hammering up on the plateau, and has been on board ship here for a few days' convalescence. With a black beard and moustache I hardly recognised him, and he's thin as a ghost. So I invited him to dine with us

99

before he went back to his regiment.

I must say we must have looked a thorough set of ruffians. Sam Park, our other guest, was the only clean-shaven one among us. I'm getting up a tremendous red beard that, if nothing else, will come in handy to stuff one of our plush chairs when I get home! I actually enjoyed the dinner. Henry had bought a sheep off a steamer just in, and we had its liver, heart etc., eked out with fried pork. After that, no end of choices: Fortnum and Mason marmalade was followed by a splendid cheese from the same stable. We topped up with chocolate! As to wine, I assure you, I was able to come out in style. We used my new damask tablecloth, along with the knives and forks you had put up for me.

Giving a meal to friends seems to be the idea out here: each one brings his own knife, fork and spoon and a pocket handkerchief to wipe up with! Rich, ain't it, in the middle of a war?

You have no idea of all the swells I'm seeing every day, but the bulk of them are a miserable lot. Though individually they protest the greatest anxiety for the welfare of the men, I firmly believe they would see the whole army sacrificed before they would go one iota out of their way. At all events, it will not be for want of asking if I do not get everything I need, although even that, I fear, will be only a little. The men behave nobly: they talk of having their hats knocked off by a ball or a bullet going through the tails of their coats as a good joke, and their fortitude under sickness beats everything. But the way the animals are treated out here would wring your heart.

I think constantly about you and the dear chicks, and feel wretched at being parted from you, especially at this time with the new baby coming.

With kindest regards to Eliza Bernard and dearest love to yourself and the children, believe me ever your affectionate and loving husband,
James Beatty.

PS Let all the bills stand over till Camidge gets here and I will write you what to do. Mr. Christian will pay in monthly into my bank account the whole of my salary—£125. JB.

11

THE NAVVIES!

2ⁿᵈ February

I heard the singing as soon as I rounded the Post Office building. Though distant, it was borne clear and ringing across the water: *Cheer, boys, cheer*! I stopped in my tracks, hardly daring to believe my ears. Then I saw *Wildfire*, first and smallest of our navvy fleet, edging round Castle Point, towed by two paddle tugs which were turning her slowly into harbour towards the Ordnance Wharf.

Sam Park's fusilier 'volunteers' dropped their work behind the projected railway wharf and watched the steady approach of the ship. *Cheer, boys, cheer!* Donald waved frantically across the freshly-flattened ground. I ran to join him on the quay. 'She's made it,' I remember shouting again and again at the top of my voice as we pumped hands in total delight. Then we stood side by side watching her draw nearer, her sails close furled. The whole of her rigging was clogged with gesticulating navvies; the deck was awash with men and baggage:

> *Cheer, boys, cheer! No more of idle sorrow!*
> *Courage, true hearts, shall bear us on our way!*
> *Hope points before, and shows the bright tomorrow!*
> *Let us forget the darkness of today.*

The fusiliers waved their shovels aloft in salute. Sam Park joined us, clapping me on the shoulder. 'An answer to prayer,' he said quietly: he knew just how relieved I felt.

Bob Shaw was easy to pick out, standing beside Captain Woodward in the bows: he acknowledged my wave with ecstatic arms. 'There's one man who'll be glad to get his feet on dry land,' said Donald with a chuckle. 'Wait till he samples our mud,' was my rejoinder.

But now, thanks to Sam Park and his men, we had a flat, prepared area ready to take any quantity of stores and equipment. This transformation—in less than six days—of a dilapidated garden swamp into a level yard, hard-rammed and with a near professional surface of stones, had been wholly wrought by the toil of these men of 39th Foot. Spurred on by their two lieutenants, who were as enthusiastic as Sam himself, one of their gangs had also made a pretty fair start at cutting out a shelf on the hill for our navvies' huts. In traditional army style they had somehow scrounged barrows and even the odd bullock and cart to shift the spoil.

I had several times been tempted to start considering these men as 'ours', such was their drive and keenness. But two days earlier Sam had warned me that the 39th would be moving up to the front as soon as First Battalion reached Balaklava. 'That's what's rumoured,' he had said. However, 'General Rumour' had had a long campaign here, so I decided to take each day as it came. Now, with *Wildfire*'s arrival, I'd at last got the nucleus of a force answerable only to my directions—the crucial factor.

She was now turned to anchor broadside along the wharf. Then I spotted a plume of black smoke being blown over the hills of Cossack Bay. For the second time that morning a ship was rounding Castle Point. It emitted a piercing whistle. '*Hesperus*, by God, it's *Hesperus*,' shouted Donald. 'Good for Kellock: he's damn well m-made it!' We could hear her men, too, singing lustily as she followed *Wildfire* in, but her forward movement was slowing by the minute as she waited her turn to berth.

'Now I'll show these Jeremiahs on the General Staff what real work's all about,' declared Donald. His voice exuded a massive confidence. 'Crack men—a hundred and eighty crack men, all fired up to go.' The impact of them, seen now at close quarters, was overwhelming—strong-built, faces blackened by the sun and wind on the voyage, eyes alight, with only a narrowing strip of water separating them from their destination—and their destiny. Even those stalwarts of 39th seemed puny by comparison. As for Balaklava's wretched masses, one good puff from our hearties would blow them clean away!

As the gangway bumped down into place, little Bob Shaw fairly sprinted down it and headed for us. There was no stemming his torrent of words nor his excitement at being the first arrival. He had caught a glimpse of *Hesperus*, he said, only as they were leaving the Sea of Marmara and learnt she would be delayed an extra day for coaling at Constantinople. Then it had been a tense race across the Black Sea. 'The wind held the whole way until this morning—indeed, throughout the voyage,' he said simply. He praised Captain Woodward's seamanship, and the cooks who had fed them royally at every meal.

Shaw's tone changed as he talked of the men: it was clear, though he didn't elaborate, that he had found them more than a handful and he couldn't wait to get them on solid ground again and back to strict shifts. He was relieved when I told him they would be working day and night from now on, until the job was done.

'They drank all the Berkeley and Perkins Entire we carried in the first few days,' he complained. 'Ashore at Gibraltar they developed an uncontrollable thirst for rum and liquor of the most dubious kind. If it hadn't been for the efforts of Tom Grace and of our surgeon Dr. Howes, who patched several of them up after fights, I doubt if we would have managed to get them all back on board. Talk about a randy: it was sheer pandemonium for a couple of hours.'

I tried to reassure him: he was still shaken by the memory. 'That won't happen here, once we've got the sutlers' booths cleared out.' How naive I must have been then!

I asked Donald to supervise the berthing of the steamer while I briefed Shaw on our plans. 'All men will sleep on board till their huts are up,' I called after him. 'Get Kellock over here as quickly as possible.'

Time pressed on me like the heavy clouds now scudding towards us. The smoke from *Hesperus*' funnel had veered ominously round to the north-west: I had a nightmare vision of our precious stores, unloaded on to the shore, unprotected against a ferocious downpour. Our priorities were the navvies' huts, erection of store sheds and completion of the railway wharf. Then I hoped to get the promised Jacks from the Naval Brigade to help hump equipment out of the holds. But first the shelf, cut out by the 39th for the huts, needed re-vetting and the banking on the harbour side strengthened to prevent landslip. Shaw grasped both points at a glance.

Hesperus was now lying secure alongside *Wildfire*: the two vessels made a striking picture, each with its distinguishing pennant curling eastwards from the topmast. Navvies were clambering about the rigging, gazing curiously round the tiny land-locked harbour and the straggling shacks of the town and up to the peaks of the surrounding hills, still with snow in their deep gullies. They called down excitedly to their mates below—every man jack of them decked out in his best gear, as though part of some outlandish festival. All that was missing was a band! That would have to wait: they had yet to earn their drums and trumpets as conquering heroes. In sharp contrast to this triumphal mood was a small group on the bridge of *Hesperus*—a party of four, closely shawled against the cold and with long grey skirts they tried to control. Those were our nurses, headed by the redoubtable Mrs. Williamson.

In these exhilarating moments several folk came to shake my hand and offer congratulations. Among them was Colonel Harding, the new town commandant, and his assistant, Major Hall, a sharp and energetic-looking officer. A Captain Powell introduced himself as being now, he said, responsible for all harbour management. He was greatly exercised that we should leave space for the trooper *Medway*, expected any day with a sorely-needed draft—First Battalion, 71st Regiment. I told him it would take several days to clear our stores, and to bear in mind our other ships which would be coming shortly—hopefully by then we would have completed our new railway wharf and would be self-contained. His response was to turn curtly on his heel.

My warmest handshakes were reserved for John Kellock and for Captain Raymond, superintendent of our fleet and a man with an air of calm assurance—the ideal fellow, it struck me, to soothe the ruffled harbour-master. My attention was more caught, however, by Kellock. Certainly his manner seemed as resolute as I recollected it from those days in the Waterloo Road office but there was something in his eyes that slightly dismayed me. He looked almost as though he had been dealt a body blow. It didn't seem just like the after-effects of sea-sickness, though *Hesperus*, starting a week after *Wildfire*, had had a rough passage the whole way out. The story of that voyage emerged gradually as he spoke. In essence, the navvies had been slow to shake down together. It was the old tale of competing gangs—from the Tilbury line, the Victoria Docks, the Oxford and Worcester, and men from several other workings up and down the country.

They first showed their spirit by running amok at Gibraltar where, blind with drink, they tried to catch the apes on the Rock. One of the gangers—none other than 'Black Jack' Kemp—had even pulled out a knife when restrained. They had finally run out of money, and at that Kellock ran out of patience. At Malta, he had refused point blank to give any advance against pay but didn't stop them going ashore. Of course, they promptly outwitted him by organising exhibition boxing-bouts and cadging contributions towards prize money from amused bystanders.

They staggered back on board, with black eyes, bruises from the harbour police and sundry cuts to arms and faces for the surgeon to sew up. Then, mercifully, they were laid low for five days as the ship slipped east through choppy, corkscrewing seas. One of the redeeming features of this sorry trip, it appeared, had been the sterling work of Mrs. Williamson and the three nurses, who had quickly formed a team, doling out ointment, pills and soup and the equally strong medicine of domestic discipline—all this to men who had long before shrugged off all attempts at domestic restraint. 'They took it like lambs,' added Kellock, with a faint flicker of amusement. A real surprise packet had been William Hart—the hairdresser whom he had recruited the day before the ship sailed from Blackwall dock. 'He's an original; small and springy as a pixie,' he said. 'Look, there he is now, up on the bridge, playing his eternal penny whistle. And he's a damn good barber: he demonstrated on one of the lads while I was interviewing him.'

By the time they reached Constantinople, Kellock went on, Barber Bill had become a kind of mascot for the navvies—a teller of outlandish tales, and singer of all manner of songs!

The 'mascot' was now skipping nimbly down the iron stairway, chaffing his comrades as he descended. On reaching the deck they clustered round him as he gave a fine tenor rendering of *Oh, Judy, dear*.

After checking that Sam Park's men were busy again at the railway wharf, I took Kellock and Shaw back to our quarters for a briefing over some bread and cheese. 'We'll get nothing out of the men till they're warm and well fed in their new huts. Meanwhile they'll sleep on board, but we'll start shift working at once—with a night shift, too. That's to be our style until the job is finished.' I told them to get a tally of names to the Commissary-General's office immediately so that all men would be entered for rations. 'I'll sign the sheets, but do a duplicate for me. Mr. Filder's clerks need to be watched. Everything has to be done by the book: you'd never think there was a war on.'

Donald came in as Kellock and Shaw were leaving. 'There'll s-soon be room for you chaps near us,' he remarked with a grin. 'Another of our Turkish comrades has just been carried out next door. He only went down with cholera yesterday.' Kellock turned rather green but said nothing. It would take more than one or two of my blue pills to pull him together, I reckoned.

'A sky and wind like this means certain snow tonight,' said Donald calmly. My mind flashed to the open hatches, the hut sections to be got out, the shovels, the wheelbarrows; above all, the tarpaulins as a shield against swift-drifting snow. I could feel myself becoming obsessed with the need to protect our equipment. Any normal port could have handled our small cargoes in minutes; here everything had to be dragged out laboriously by totally untrained men. But they were all I had and precious few, as yet. Even if Lord Stratford's reneging Croats had materialised they would have been equally hamfisted: Captain Lushington's promised sailors hadn't yet shown up.

My mind raced on: the surgeons and nurses required huts; we'd need a medical centre, quickly. I'd seen enough of Balaklava hospital treatment to have no faith in it for our kind of accidents or emergencies.

'Snow before nightfall, for sure.' Donald raised his voice to cut through the ceaseless babble from the street, 'Jim, I want to get markers in right through the town while I can still see the ground.' Henry jumped to his feet. 'I'll have a gang, markers and all the gear back here in half an hour,' he said in one quick breath as he darted to the door. 'Pick up Wright as you go,' Donald shouted after him.

Henry's action broke the gloomy logjam of my thoughts: I resolved never again to think along those lines. We'd finish the job we'd set ourselves—on time—if it had to be done on our knees. My resolution was to be tested immediately: all activity at our new railway wharf had ceased abruptly; the men of the 39th were cleaning off their shovels, stacking them against empty barrows and forming into line, urged on by an officer. Captain Park, when he reached me, could hardly look me in the face. 'So sorry, Mr. Beatty,' he blurted out. 'We've been recalled by the adjutant: the regiment is to move forward: a Russian attack's rumoured. I wish you the best of luck.'

We shook hands; his men marched off. I had had their assistance for five days...so much for even the most willing military cooperation!

That night I half-dozed in my office chair, planning work schedules for the coming days. One thing was certain: to stay out of mischief, our navvies had to be kept at full stretch. I listened to the wind gusting against the roof whose creaking sounded ominous. Light from a candle reflected the snowflakes whirling down the street past our broken window. They seemed to be falling faster by the minute...

1. James Beatty 1820–1856, engineer-in-chief Crimean War Railway. (Photograph of watercolour painted in 1854 just before he left for the front: from Wallace Beatty, great-grandson.)

3. Thomas Brassey 1805–1870, railway contractor, partner in PB&B.

2. Sir Morton Samuel Peto Bt. 1809–1889, senior partner in Peto, Brassey & Betts (PB&B), railway contractors.

4. Edward Ladd Betts 1815–1872, partner in PB&B, married to Sir Morton Peto's youngest sister.

5. Navvies milling about outside the offices of PB&B in Waterloo Road, London, in response to the appeal for labour for the Crimea.

6. The men bidding farewell and signing over a portion of their wages to their families before boarding the train at Euston Square terminus, bound for Liverpool, Birkenhead and the Crimea.

7. The first of the railway fleet, the clipper, Wildfire, *leaves Birkenhead docks on 21st December with men and supplies for the railway.*

8. *Viscount Stratford de Redcliffe, Ambassador to Constantinople – 'The Sublime Porte'. (Chalk drawing 1853 by Geo. Richmond.)*

9. *Street scene in Balaklava before the hurricane, described to Beatty prior to his arrival there.*

10. The Navvies' first task was to build their own huts high on a hill overlooking Balaklava town, which entailed heavy banking.

11. Night scene outside the town where work continued night and day for several weeks in order to achieve Sir Morton Peto's pledge to the Prime Minister of 'seven miles of track in seven weeks'.

12. Balaklava main street showing railway running alongside the harbour. (From a lithograph by William Simpson.)

13. Field Marshal Lord Raglan, KCB, 1788–1855, Fitzroy James Henry Somerset 1st Baron, C-in-C Crimea. (Photograph by Roger Fenton 1855.)

14. 'Turning out for the Trenches.'
Rifle Brigade soldier bare-foot in snow
in Crimean War; from watercolour by
W.J. Colville, January 1855.

15. W.H. Russell, The Times corre-
spondent. (Photograph by Roger
Fenton, Crimea 1855.)

16. Navvies loading a wagon with sleepers and rail in the yard at Balaklava for
the extending of the track up to the front line. A spare cable-winding drum for the
stationary engines lies on the right.

17. Dray horses pulling a wagonload of hut sections along the railway line out of Balaklava (navvies aloft) towards Kadikoi. Frenchman's Hill ahead, old road on right.

18. Wagonloads being pulled along railway line past the Sutlers' Bazaar (Vanity Fair) at Donnybrook, Kadikoi.

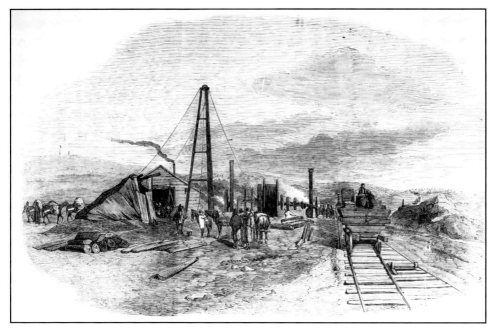

19. *Stationary engines at work pulling wagons up towards the final slope to Headquarters, which is where the trucks ran away down the hill throwing Beatty and others out. The engines also operated the artesian drill on the left.*

20. *James Beatty (right) and Donald Campbell standing on the track in Balaklava railway yard. (Photograph by Roger Fenton probably taken after they rescued all his valuable equipment, which had been unloaded on to the quayside in bad weather, and transported it on the railway to his quarters.)*

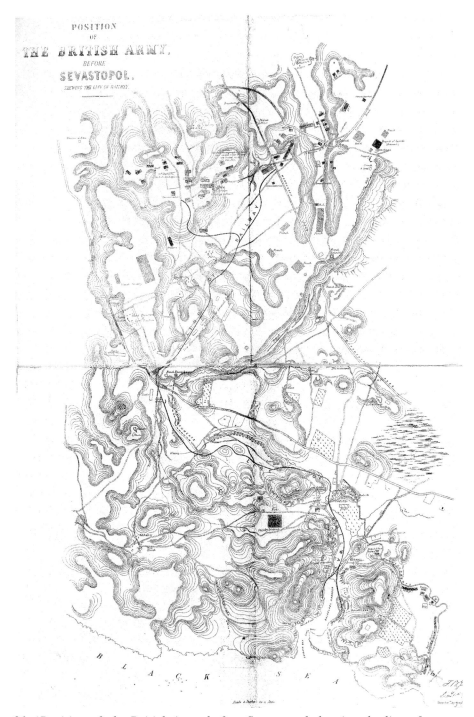

21. 'Position of the British Army before Sevastopol shewing the line of Railway'. From the plan communicated to the War Department, signed, James Beatty, C.E. 13th April 1855. Scale 4 inches to a mile. (Photocopy of original.)

12

BUILD UP AND BREAK OUT

8ᵗʰ February

The walls of Jericho began to fall that morning, not to the sound of trumpets but to the shattering blows of the navvies' sledgehammers. It was the first day of our carefully-planned operation through the town and out on to the Balaklava plain.

At dawn the first shift swung into action. The men had been selected after long discussion with Tom Grace and Dikkon Brown, our most experienced gangers, and their choice of teams was surprising. Both had settled for what could be an explosive mixture.

Dikkon had picked his gang from men of the Tilbury line and the Victoria Docks, blended with some old Norwich-Lowestoft stalwarts. Tom had settled for his old Dorset gang and a sprinkling of the Nova Scotia men who only a few days before had been at each other hammer-and-tongs on the ship, and were still showing the after-effects. He had left Kemp and his men for Matt Bennett to fit into his all-important night shift.

The snow certainly seemed to have smoothed over their differences, at least for the time being: they behaved like children in it— but had the essential revetting and banking done in a trice. Hut sections were quickly swung out of the holds; ten for the men and one for the gangers, besides a store shed and kitchen. There was no need to urge speed: everyone saw it starkly as a matter of life and death. At last we were starting to turn things our way. Barber Bill reflected the buoyant mood: I saw him squatted on an upturned bucket, painting names on stray pieces of wood. He held up the first one for me to see: Peto Crescent, I read. Other huts were named Brighton Pier, Trafalgar Square and so on according to the men's fancy—the gangers' hut was Home, Sweet Home!

Astonishingly, the weather held fair for the whole operation—bitter nights but daytime clear skies. Huts for the surgeons and nurses began to take shape, and a medical room alongside. Albert Howes was a moving spirit in all of this, and Mrs. Williamson walked over from *Hesperus* several times a day to monitor progress. All gangs were beginning to settle into their accustomed rhythm. Even Kellock looked perkier after I had dosed him with a couple of my blue pills; Henry was having the time of his life. When not helping Donald with the line of markers which now were well out beyond the town, he was volubly conferring, in his other capacity of 'Master of the Horse' with John Parker over the layout of the stables for our precious drays. He delighted in laying down the law on horse-flesh to anyone who would listen—seasoned Hussars and Lascars alike!

Captain Lushington finally came across handsomely with 150 Jacks who carried on the slogging work started by the 39th of consolidating the rail yard. The new wharf would need piling, but that was a specialist job which would have to wait for the arrival of the ship with our pile-drivers. But there was no question: the main yard could now handle a great volume of stores. I had tarpaulins brought over as a precaution against the unbelievably dry weather abruptly reverting to pattern.

Captain George Raymond, commodore of our armada, was anxious about extra unloading berths. 'Two more of our ships at least should be here within days,' he told me, 'perhaps even three.' I tried to reassure him: 'I believe we can clear both *Wildfire*'s and *Hesperus*' stores on to the yard area in the next two days. Then we can shift those vessels away up the harbour'. I found it a hard promise to keep, for I was reluctant to divert the navvies from their present urgent job.

In the nick of time I was saved by the completely unexpected arrival from Constantinople of 750 Croat labourers. Lord Stratford's persuasion (or, more likely, pay) had finally prevailed! The town commandant allocated 200 to me. Under strict supervision—and mostly instructed by sign language—they managed to grasp the essentials of unloading holds: it was a stirring sight to see them coming down the gangplank, each one balancing a length of rail on his shoulder. Nothing seemed too heavy for those broad backs. (We were careful to see that their own cooks kept them well fed.) So the piles of plant and materials grew, and the last job each night was to see that they were securely tarpaulined down.

Thus reassured, I could concentrate on our main thrust through Balaklava. Colonel Harding, the town commandant, had approved our plan which would transform for ever that once sleepy little fishing port. He had ordered all foreigners to move out. Many Turks, too, began to make their bewildered way to Kadikoi and other smaller villages across the plain, loading bundles, cooking pots, sticks of furniture on to pitifully small animals. One felt for their heartbreak; soon only a few sickly donkeys were left, straying around the empty stinking alleys.

The predatory hordes of sutlers had been the first to heed the commandant's warning and had moved out instantly, determined to regroup on rising ground to the west of our planned route a mile or so towards Kadikoi. They had commandeered almost all the remaining animals, carts and arabas and these they had feverishly loaded with tents, hut sections, roof tiles, curtains and trestle tables. The lashes and oaths of the drivers in every language of the Middle East furnished an eerie counterpoint to the thud of the navvies' sledge-hammers.

Tom Grace marshalled his gang on the west side of the main street, a body of men who seemed like creatures from a different world—extravagantly clad, bronzed of face, loud of voice, with outlandish oaths, gripping pickaxes like so many pencils—Dikkon Brown had positioned his Tilbury and Victoria Docks men on the east of the street.

The first blows on the flimsy walls of the houses clattered like thunder, and as the roofs began to crash down clouds of plaster dust shot up into the still air like gun smoke. The volume of rubble was quickly reduced to manageable size by the next wave of Tom's men and shovelled into the roadway. There Dikkon's gang filled in the fetid pools with rocks and rubble and threw in chloride of lime. Then the remaining debris was systematically stamped down to make a wide raised bed for the double track of the line.

Work went ahead continuously throughout the day, with the

hammer gangs changing places and men breaking off for a quick bite at rations packed in their own individual cloths. In the afternoon Kellock took over supervision from me. I decided to make a start on the terminus sidings, and roughed out the route of a temporary spur to the new wharf. The sailors were pounding the rail bed to a surprisingly solid state; I switched some 30 Croats from unloading rails to fetching baskets of stones and rubble for the road foundations. In one corner of the yard the carpenters were busy at their sawing machines preparing sleepers from the rough lengths of timber brought up from the holds. Meanwhile rails, plates and spikes were coming ashore in a steady flow. It wouldn't be long before the first line of sleepers would be laid and the first rails levered into place and nailed firmly down. I would have to admit it was rough and ready stuff, but needs must...

I marvelled at our continuing luck with the weather; the cloudless sky streaked only by low-flying geese, swooping and veering as though in alarm at the changing face of a familiar landscape. I longed for just one hour with my shot-gun: but *that* was decidedly not it! High over the hills buzzards circled endlessly, oblivious of the noise of the guns that came trembling on the air.

By nightfall, the navvy gangs were already a quarter of the way through the town. The pace of the work had been speeding up and a hard drive was now in progress as the men responded to the urgency of the task. In places, the rubble reached nearly to shoulder height: ample enough material for the night-shift—now off-duty—to tamp into place. There might even be some moonlight to help the work: suddenly I remembered our braziers! As though reading my thoughts, Henry arrived, leading a line of Croats laden with just those items— also bags of charcoal, coal and wood. He set them up and then sent the men scavenging for splintered panels, broken chairs and scraps of abandoned carpet—anything that would fuel our improvised torches for the long night's labours.

As I arrived back at our quarters I came face to face with a figure I had only seen once before up on the plateau, in a snow-storm: I just about recognised him—Colonel William Ridley, Scots Fusilier Guards—a nice old fellow but now sadly pulled down. I invited him

112

inside and he sat down heavily. He told me he had just brought his regiment down: only 146 men remained of the 1,300 who had marched up in January. When he left I pressed a bottle of curacao into his hands; he looked as pleased as punch.

That night was the first of three weeks' all-night vigils for me. Henry, who every day displayed some new initiative, had procured a useful Greek cook for our small establishment. But even after a tolerable evening meal and a cigar I simply couldn't settle to cards or letter-writing like the others but had to go downstairs to the office and sit in my chair near the door: seemingly, I had lost all capacity to sleep. Every half hour or so I was out at the workings inspecting progress. Matt Bennett, the ganger in charge, made sure that the effort never faltered. He was a huge Scot who limped from an accident caused by a tree he was helping to fell on one of our Nova Scotia routes, but he was still nippy and was forever up and down his line of sweating men. I paid him a last call at five o'clock the following morning, to congratulate him on the quality of work. He sniffed the air like some wise old wolf: 'All well so far, but ye'll have but one more fine day, Mister Beatty, then the rains'll return'. His rolling 'r's' had a hint of thunder to them.

Satisfied, I went indoors, looking forward to an early breakfast. Henry had shown an unexpected side to his character by constituting himself our steward. He had quickly trained the cook in our ways, and 'Zito' had developed an effective juggling act with our scraggy rations of goat-meat and salt pork. That morning he surpassed himself with newly-baked rolls and very tolerable coffee.

Donald shared Matt's view of the weather. 'Today will have to be another big heave. We must get a line of rails started before the mud takes hold.' My concern was to get the horses ashore. 'It's the lack of skilled manpower that frets me,' I said. 'The Jacks—and the Croats too—are willing enough but they need to be led. If only we had another shipload of navvies.'

I made for the area I had marked out for the stables. There was our horsemaster John Parker, sweating profusely in a vivid yellow oilskin, frantically chivvying on a string of Croat labourers who were manhandling solid wooden sections, supervised by a couple of our carpenters. 'I had 'em roust these out from *Hesperus* first thing; them horses can't stay aboard for ever,' he shouted, 'so I've got a gang together to erect 'em.' And indeed he had, a laughing gang at that, who willingly set about squaring up the main block. When finished it would be a formidable structure and would need to be, initially to shelter our present 35 drays, and with two further blocks to cope with later reinforcements from England. There would be a separate store shed for grain and hay: already I saw several bales laid out on dry planks in position, firmly protected by tarpaulins from wind and rain. John was bothered in his mind about how to get the horses ashore. 'Easy enough at Blackwall, with dock-side cranes,' he said anxiously. I promised I'd think about the problem. Not for the first time that morning I wished fervently that Edgar Swan would arrive in *Humboldt*: that had a crane of sorts we could, at a pinch, shift across to *Hesperus*.

Everywhere I looked the scene was one of purposeful activity and noise. I was glad we'd shipped so many rammers, though I'd never envisaged them being wielded by sailors; supplied with load after load of shingle and stones by the Croats, they were on the way to producing a credit-worthy surface for the new wharf; it felt reassuringly solid as I stamped on it. All that was needed now was the final piling to edge the harbour wall. When finished, I reckoned that two ships could discharge broadside along its length. Already under Donald's supervision the first spur of the line was taking shape towards the main terminus area.

I decided to run a short spur to serve the fuel store south of the stables, and continue a single track along past Russell's house through the Ordnance Yard and alongside their store. Looking further south towards the ruins of the old castle I wondered yet again why the Commissary-General had elected to site his main sheds so inconveniently at the very end of a rough track. Perhaps, I thought spitefully, it was because it was adjoined by a handsome detached house where Mr. Filder himself resided in some style, shielded from all but the most persistent visitors. Please God it wouldn't be too long before we made a start on the branch up the west side of the harbour: but that would have to wait for the arrival of our miners.

Still, there was plenty to keep everyone occupied; all were imbued with a spirit of urgency. I could hear the steady thump of the rammers long before I reached the main street which looked as though it had been struck by an earthquake. The day shifts had switched places; Dikkon Brown's gang was attacking the houses on the west side with well-timed blows that breached walls and rocked the battered structures—they themselves survivors of hurricanes and years of ravage by rain and wind. Today, though, the plaster dust was not rising straight but blowing in wavering lines across the roofs towards the east of the town.

Tom Grace greeted me with an optimistic smile: 'Us'll be more than two parts through this town come tomorrow morning, sir.' 'The sooner we're out on the plain the better,' I replied. 'Look at that sky.' Black clouds were massing swiftly over the western horizon. Without a word, Tom turned back to the road up which his men were advancing. To speed the work he had collared a few of the brighter Croats and, by gesture alone, was patiently instructing them how best to shovel small pieces of plaster and stone smoothly ahead of the line of ramming navvies. Communication might have been no more than an occasional slap on the back or an encouraging shout but it kept those labourers pegging solidly away.

A great thing—communication! Then I thought one could as easily have non-comprehension even when the two parties were conversing in the same language—namely myself and our Commissary-General!

But there was no doubt that I was singularly unhappy with the French tongue, and this had become only too apparent during my long journey down the Med in the French trooper. Until I started having lessons from that obliging young lieutenant all I could muster were phrases—often only swear words—in rusty French-Canadian patois picked up when in the Maritime Provinces. I decided to resume lessons as soon as possible: that language deserved to be treated as seriously as Latin when I, as a boy, was being taught it by my father. Thinking of some of my engineering contemporaries, like Buddicom and Mackenzie, now managing large railway enterprises in the heart of France, I felt ashamed of my ineptitude.

Russell ('Master' Russell, as he called himself) was one who found French a most useful tool for picking up scraps of information, carrying it off smoothly with his jovial personality. Gossip and rumour were all grist to his journalistic mill—and rated as such—but I was glad of his reassurance on one point the other day at lunch. I was deeply concerned about a possible Russian threat to Kadikoi—our expedition was, after all, in a war zone. An attack could have grave consequences for our line, about which they had had ample advance warning. Russell felt the threat far-fetched: we were strong in defence there, he declared, with reinforcements building up daily. Any enemy thrust from the Tchernaya River would give our troops at least a day's warning. But I was still uneasy about the attention our night-shift flares strung across the plain would attract. I was very aware, too, of our position as an unarmed civilian corps: how soon, I wondered, would pressure be exerted on me to permit our force to be used to buttress military efforts in one way or another? I remembered all my urgent pleadings back home to establish our clear status as civilians— my only safeguard for undivided control.

The matter would, however, be raised much more swiftly than I expected.

Back at our quarters I found Albert Howes and Ethelbert Blake who were enjoying a 'surgeon's holiday' discussing emergency operations they had carried out. 'I'm back to the 55th this afternoon,' said Ethelbert, 'and I've brought a little gift for you.' He went outside and untied from the saddle of his horse a fair-sized ham and a mound of oranges. 'He's got better yarns than mine,' remarked Howes, 'but then he's been longer at the business.'

'You shouldn't be going back so soon,' I warned Ethelbert. 'There's no flesh on you at all.'

'I've more on me than some,' he replied sombrely. He told us he had been haunted while convalescing on *Orion* by memories of the men he had tried to treat in the front line. He showed me a piece of leather, almost bitten through. This was all that remained of a gag he had used on a patient to stop his screams while he amputated a leg. 'The lucky ones were caught in snipers' crossfire or blown sky-high by bursting shells. Any I could patch up would spend days in a

116

leaking tent on sodden ground without a blanket under their body. Then they'd be carted to a primitive field unit. That was frequently their death sentence.'

Ethelbert spent his days scrounging for bandages and the most basic of drugs. 'Our regiment has only lost one-third of its fighting strength during the whole winter,' he said proudly. His views on the General Medical Staff were sulphurous: 'I'd string up the lot of them, starting with Sir John Hall, on the highest masts in the harbour. If it wasn't for Miss Nightingale, there wouldn't be a single fighting soldier left by now!'

'That's why I'm going back up again: when you've once seen the condition of the troops there's nothing else to do,' he said, simply. 'Some are doing sentry duty in bare feet. As for fire fuel, I've known several cases where the men have dried their salt beef rations into strips and burned them to boil water for coffee.'

We waved him off as he trotted slowly in the direction of the plateau.

All through that night the rail bed was being packed tight and driven ahead down the street. On my half-hourly visits, Matt Bennett had encouraging progress to report. 'I've sweated the roughness out of most,' he remarked, 'but I'm keeping my eye on one of 'em. That Jack Kemp: he's a sullen, vicious sod, and over-free with his fists.' It was difficult to make out faces in the flickering light of the braziers, but I could clearly see the menacing figure of Kemp driving his gang forward with curses. Well, not everyone was sweet-tempered at 4 am.

Our luck with the weather continued. Despite a massive build-up of cloud we sneaked another dry day. It couldn't last, and I drove every man to his limit. The priorities were simple: clear everything from the holds, except for the horses in *Hesperus*; get roofs on the main store sheds, the stable block and the medical huts. I set the Jacks to squaring up the new wharf and the main yard: one detachment joined the Croats in bringing off rails, timber and the heavier gear. Whatever they were asked they did with a will. Even the Croats caught some of the sailors' enthusiasm and their infectious camaraderie. Alas, it was to be their last service: Captain Lushington sent an order through his steward switching the tars next day to haul siege guns up to the plateau.

I returned for the last time at 5.30 am satisfied that the last houses on the route were being razed in clouds of smoke and that the rail bed was finally clear of the town and heading for Kadikoi. As I turned towards our quarters a drop of icy rain splashed on to my forehead. Before I could hurry indoors I was soaked to the skin.

13

UP AND RUNNING

16th February

Rain was our staple diet for the next three days: it saturated everything—food, clothing, but not our spirits. Then, with the bitter wind swinging north, came sleet in continuous sheets. The exodus of riffraff from the town had by now almost ceased, but each day brought the familiar slow straggle of ration parties and benumbed sick and wounded down from the front lines. Undeterred by the vicious change in weather, our gangs stuck at their tasks, their high boots more than a match for the engulfing mud. Everywhere a grey curtain of rain hung like smoke above the ground.

At the far end of the street Tom Grace greeted me exultantly: 'They're well into their stride now, sir. We'll be across that plain before you can say knife.'

'An unfortunate word that, knife,' I said. 'I don't know quite what's getting into the men, Tom; there seem to be more wrong 'uns than I bargained for.'

'It's the drink those sutlers are selling at their new camp,' cried Tom vehemently. 'They'll walk miles for it, even after a full shift: it turns 'em hysterical.'

'Hysterical—our navvies?'

Tom nodded: 'Yes, and fighting drunk. It's a mercy they don't fancy the women on offer.'

Suddenly Donald loomed out of the fog, at a run. 'They've arrived; our ships—I think *three* of them! Can't you hear the whistles?' From the Ordnance Wharf the noise rolled eerily across the water. Shielding my eyes I could just make out three dim shapes, anchored well out. 'They've only come in this last half hour,' he said excitedly, 'screw s-steamers—*Prince of Wales*,

Baron von Humboldt and the *Earl of Durham*!'

Three steamers packed with navvies! Their arrival nearly trebled our labour force at a stroke. And on the second, I knew, would be Edgar Swan, with his engineers and fitters; also our storekeeper and an assistant surgeon.

'*Wildfire*'s hold is cleared now,' I said to Donald. 'I'll get Captain Woodward to shift her, so that *Humboldt* can come in alongside *Hesperus*, and Swan can get his crane across. Then we'll take the horses ashore tomorrow.' I asked Donald to get Swan and Harry Compton, our time-keeper on *Humboldt*, to row ashore at once, and to arrange a general staff briefing at my office. 'Let the two surgeons report to Dr. Howes.'

On *Wildfire* I found our chief surgeon below, putting back a Croat labourer's dislocated shoulder. 'I'll be glad of help,' he said when I told him the news. 'I want to turn the navvies' old sleeping quarters on this ship into a regular hospital ward. I've a notion, too, for a kind of portable surgery: we can rig it up in a tent and move it forward as the work goes on.' I approved of that. I myself had plans for *Wildfire* which I had decided to keep as a permanent expedition ship here at Balaklava: I intended to convert part of the hold into something of a chapel for our two scripture readers' Sunday services.

I had developed the habit of visiting the various working parties on horseback, to save time; it reminded me strongly of my father doing his routine rounds in the old trap pulled by Tess, and accompanied by his inseparable companion, Bounce, our pet terrier. There were never any such dogs here; the few remaining were all flea-ridden, mangey and wild—or mad.

I rode to the north end of the harbour where Major Hall had told me the small vessel housing the Croats was berthed. 'Strictly, it's only intended for two hundred and fifty men, but there are three times as many on board. They threatened the captain with knives yesterday, but the Provost Marshal's men took them off in short order.'

The rest seemed peaceable enough to me, strapping fellows huddled together in multi-coloured clothes in the half-gloom below deck. Small groups were noisily playing cards, but most just lay there, eyes shut, smoking their long pipes, looking the very picture of off-duty indolence. I silently blessed Lord Stratford: in the end he had proved as good as his word. My 200 Croats were beginning to prove of value, and I'd managed to persuade Major Hall to earmark a further 300 for work on the western side of the harbour, clearing away rocks once my miners had started to blast the overhanging cliffs. The stone there, I had noticed, had a distinctive sparkle to it: the name Diamond Wharf seemed appropriate.

The door of the new medical hut was opened promptly by our chief nurse Mrs. Williamson, who was still smiling apparently at some remark by one of the nurses. They were laughing together as they emptied crates of medicines and arranged them on shelving along the back wall, under the keen eye of Dick Brazier, our medical stock keeper. 'That's our dispensary,' she said with satisfaction. We were standing in what was obviously the reception area. The whole scene took me back vividly to the hastily-erected outbuildings at my father's cholera hospital. Two stretchers stood in one corner; a chair was beside the small table on which were a pitcher, tin basin and roll of coloured towelling.

So far, Mrs. Williamson said, they hadn't been very busy: 'A few cuts for stitching, a broken nose or two—the normal navvy way of conducting an argument. You could say they're all fighting fit, Mr. Beatty,' she added with a smile. I warned her of the new shiploads of men just arrived, as she took me through the sheeting rain along precarious planks to the nurses' quarters. 'I would be glad to have a covered way,' she remarked, as we went into the hut. It was plainly though adequately furnished, with double bolts on door and windows. Mrs. Williamson and her team would be more than a match for any number of hysterical navvies I thought, as I looked at her kindly but determined face. My opinion of Dr. Howes as a picker of staff rose sharply.

Hysterical navvies, navvies who were prepared to use knives: it all made for uneasy thoughts, for these were the same men I had chosen and who had to work to the limit, continuously. Yet some form of leisure time had to be built in—on Sundays possibly, as on normal railway contracts—but the thought of idle hours, however well merited, brought up an ugly vision of the sutlers and those stalls of temptation. Their settlement strung right alongside our route to Kadikoi hadn't got its nickname of 'Vanity Fair' for nothing. I would have to talk frankly to my colleagues and the gangers about this problem, and then make things plain to the men, who would in any event be finding their first experience of the Crimea jolting enough.

Donald had rounded up everybody for the briefing meeting by the time I arrived, except Henry who was following on from the main yard. He and Kellock had that morning begun to make admirable sense of the track layout whose main directions were marked by lines of sleepers, brought from the sawing machines in a continuous stream on the shoulders of our Croats. The southern stretch had almost reached the Ordnance Wharf, and platelayers and navvies were nudging the glistening lengths of rail into position for connection and final spiking. While not neglecting work on the sidings, Kellock had set himself and his men the task by nightfall of thrusting the track north to link with the rail bed through the town.

All navvies relished having a goal; each was determined to prove himself a '20-ton-a-day' man. The rain that streamed off their sou'westers was utterly ignored in their headlong drive across the thick mud.

I sensed a cooler atmosphere in our quarters though Edgar Swan seemed his normal bright self. He had brought a most providential game pie with him; everyone was crowded round the table tucking in. The two surgeons, Kay and Roberts, had joined Albert Howes on *Wildfire*, as had George Gyngell, our second scripture reader, Donald reported. It was good to have our steady timekeepers, Harry Compton and Bill Curry, again with the party—and Bill Cole, most meticulous of storekeepers. 'You've just got here in time to stop things getting out of hand,' I told him, and got a grin in return.

'Mr. Beatty, I don't know whether you remember me!' The voice came from a small, wrinkled man who was perched on our only sofa at the far end of the room, looking nervously out of the window at the rain. 'Charles Camidge, from head office. I've brought my three assistant cashiers—Lewis, Middleton and Bartlett.' I remembered Jim Lewis as a steady and obliging clerk who had looked after my own salary affairs, but Camidge himself was a more distant figure in the counting-house at Great George Street. I was put off by his querulous tone, and wondered why on earth Edward Betts had picked him out specially.

'We were given first-class passages to Malta,' he went on, 'but there we were positively hustled aboard *Earl of Durham* and the service was very poor: I was forced to complain to the Captain. "Operational urgency" was the only excuse he vouchsafed.' That was a long speech from a little man, obviously bewildered at finding himself pitchforked into a wholly strange and unexpected out-station. Camidge was old but not as elderly as Filder; nevertheless, I detected in him something of a similar blinkered attitude.

'There's a war going on here,' I replied curtly, my mind on more important issues than one man's comfort. The briefing I then gave was to the point and was listened to attentively. At its end my colleagues moved off smartly to set plans in motion: the navvies were to be got ashore at once and formed into gangs. There was to be no repetition of the snarling and brawling that had occurred on *Hesperus*.

Early the following morning I rode over to the wharf, to find John Parker supervising the unloading of the first of our shires. The huge animal was swung out perilously over the side, but the broad restraining canvas under shoulders and belly held firm, and he was set down light as a feather on the quay to be made much of by John. Edgar Swan gave the thumbs up from the deck. Later, I saw the first arrivals being settled into the new stables, all looking out inquisitively over their half-doors. The cribs had been filled with hay, and even straw strewn under hoof. Names had been painted above each stall— Big Tom, Bess, Skittles, Pipkin, Dapple—these, I heard later, the work of our artistic barber: Bill was leaving his mark everywhere!

My site office looked workmanlike, and in the small hut Henry Stone was turning out drawings for Donald. Some instinct must have prompted me to site Camidge's accommodation further away. I only rated him fifteen shillings to the pound: he would bear watching. So would Kellock, I thought, though for a different reason. Able and willing as he was, after his experience with the navvies on the voyage I felt I shouldn't put too much pressure on him.

Behind the railway wharf our line of store sheds was rising in a solid phalanx. Luckily, the foundations had been put down before the rain started, and now our carpenters were swarming up ladders, whisking away protective tarpaulins and slotting roof sections into place. Some of the smaller sheds still sported distinctive liveries, South Eastern and Midland Counties among them. Edward Betts in his frantic search had thankfully swept up all gifts from the home railway companies, including a mixed set of wagons, some awaiting wheels, and drums of wire rope from the Victoria Docks for the winding engines.

Edgar Swan had quietly commandeered an empty shed for the assembly of the first stationary engine which had been carried across in pieces by the Croats. His fitters were itching to give it a trial, an operation watched by a silent ring of children who moved away in alarm as the engine began to emit smoke, but remained, fascinated. It was a relief to see it working so sweetly: one of Swan's engineers pulled the whistle which let forth an alarming series of shrieks. This was our very first piece of machinery to be set up on enemy soil—I was proud of that wholly civilian initiative!

Leaving the fitters assembling the second engine I took Swan off to see our bed of ballast outside the town. He told me he had just been offered some casual Turkish labour: they would be ideal for loading the stores into panniers on the few commissariat mules we had, for distribution along the track. Once rails were firmly fixed, our night gangs could then ram ballast down between the sleepers, giving firm footing for the horses drawing loaded wagons.

'I'll get the pile-drivers off the ship next,' said Swan, and hurried back.

'Good, I need them,' I replied. The most urgent task was to get ballast dumped along the route over the plain. We couldn't risk the track being washed away: it would all have to be consolidated, of course, but later on.

By next day our line of rails filled the complete length of the widened main street connecting with the terminus layout, and the rail bed was heading north out of the town towards Kadikoi. As an unexpected bonus, the rain had decided to slacken. Donald and Henry came in, soaked but contented, after a satisfactory day's survey of the half-mile incline up Frenchman's Hill. The route would necessitate extra cuttings, but they'd come across a couple of beds of workable stone. They reported heavy rifle fire by both sides, with a prolonged mortar barrage in the afternoon. Some balls fell near the French entrenchments, but no shots had reached their position.

The scene that night, as the rain finally ceased, resembled some strange native dance, with the figures of Matt Bennett's night shift silhouetted eerily in the braziers' flames, shovels glinting, and the steady drum-beat of rammers.

I was out early next morning with Swan to assess the ground ahead. As expected, it was spongy, with rain water lying on the flat surfaces. Several of the rivulets were so deep that an animal's leg could easily get broken if it stumbled, but our route beside the old rough track was not too much affected. The first obstacle was a fast-flowing stream some 200 yards out of the town. I asked Swan to get his men to bring a pile-driver piecemeal right up to the bank so that piers could quickly be driven in for the stout wooden bridge we required. It was quickly assembled and put to work.

By next afternoon Skittles and Pipkin had hauled their first load of rails, sleepers and timber along the newly-laid line, and the rail bed was being vigorously extended to the far side of the stream. A drying wind blew from the south-west. John Wright and his carpenters were assembling the bridging beams which they had pre-cut and bored for easy bolting. Swan knew of my intention to double-track the line to Kadikoi and he had made suitable provision for that in the initial width of his piers. It was a matter of an hour to get them rammed in firmly on both sides.

His engineers were busily dismantling the machine when I heard someone call my name: I turned round to see a fresh-faced young cavalry officer picking his way towards me across the boggy ground. 'I'm Burghersh,' he explained, 'one of Lord Raglan's ADCs, Mr. Beatty. His Lordship is anxious to have a few moments' talk with you, if convenient.'

I glanced over his shoulder to the old track; there, surrounded by a small group of staff officers, was indeed the Commander-in-Chief himself. It was the first encounter of many I was to have with Lord

Raglan over the months ahead, and it struck me then how typical of his personality, as I later came to know it, was the initial appearance he presented. It was one of self-effacement, almost of anonymity. He had on a voluminous grey waterproof and wore a battered forage cap. His horse, too, was a grey, an elderly animal whose head hung low in weariness. A couple of his officers had mired jackets, after unlucky tumbles no doubt on the way down from headquarters, and all the horses' legs were solidly caked with mud.

'Mr. Beatty, good morning to you,' Lord Raglan began, bending down in the saddle and putting out his left arm—his only arm—to shake my hand. It was a firm but brief grip. 'Not the most relaxed place to meet in, nor enough time, I'm afraid, for all the questions I wanted to put to you. It has taken longer than planned to get down here this morning, and I've a staff meeting on *Caradoc* shortly.' His manner was pleasant, and his face had an open, kindly expression. He gestured towards the men at the bridge and our gangs working on the roadbed beyond. 'You have made remarkable progress in such a short time, Mr. Beatty.'

I was about to voice my disappointment at the total lack of army support, but judged this was not an opportune moment. As though sensing some such interjection, he went on: 'When do you expect to reach Kadikoi?'

'By 23rd February, sir,' I replied, 'when we plan to start carrying stores to the new depot there.'

'Do you hear that, Burgoyne?' he said to a tall staff officer beside him.

'I did indeed, sir, but one must always bear weather in mind, however, and the likelihood of Russian attacks.'

'Of course, of course,' muttered Lord Raglan. He looked somewhat put out by that comment.

'Might I stay, sir,' added Sir John, 'to speak with Mr. Beatty on another matter?'

The Commander-in-Chief nodded, giving me a small smile and saying he would like to examine our arrangements in detail when he came down next, in a day or two.

His chief engineer dismounted and drew himself up stiffly,

looking every one of his reputed seventy-three years. It was astonishing to think of such an old man still holding high command in that campaign. Deep furrows on his bitter face darkened the sallow skin. He came straight to the point: 'I hear, Mr. Beatty, you were displeased when I didn't chair the Board of Officers the other day. I'm sorry: I was at the C-in-C's military council meeting. Nevertheless, it seems you had your way.'

'It could hardly have been otherwise, Sir John: the route I selected really spoke for itself. I had, however, hoped for more understanding and cooperation from the officers on the Board.'

'But they concurred with your view, I believe,' replied Sir John, a trifle defensively.

'When I spoke of cooperation I had very much in mind the Duke of Newcastle's instructions to Lord Raglan to offer *all* assistance to the expedition. When I requested *temporary* help from the army in the way of labour until my navvies arrived I was told it was impossible.'

'You are surely aware, Mr. Beatty, of the present manpower situation? No spare men were available for such a purpose.'

I ignored this comment, and continued: 'Had it not been for a hundred and fifty volunteers generously offered by 39th Regiment, we would have been totally stranded. As it was, those men and their three willing officers were withdrawn after six days. Captain Lushington later provided me with a handsome body of Jacks who did great service—and then I received an unexpected addition of untrained Croat labour, courtesy of Lord Stratford.'

'I'm sure the Board of Officers did all in their power, sir.' Clearly the topic was at an end. 'However,' Sir John continued, 'I wish to raise another matter with you, one very much related to the army's present situation. You will soon have at your command some four or five hundred navvies—fine fellows all of them: I should like to suggest that they might advantageously be enrolled so that they could support our troops in defence of positions wherever they might happen to be.'

The bald proposal took my breath away: I looked hard at Sir John, wondering for an instant whether he was being ironic, but his manner was serious enough. Neither time nor place were suited for deep philosophical discussion: I therefore stated our position with complete candour: 'That matter, sir, was fully discussed by us with the Government in London, and it was then decided *not* to arm the men. They were—rightly, in my opinion—regarded as too valuable to be employed as soldiers, and they were distinctly told that they would not be called upon to fight. Asking those men to volunteer now would be a breach of faith: those not disposed to such a course would be driven to do so by jeers from those who were. The result would be to disrupt them altogether as useful workmen.'

'Mine was purely a personal suggestion for your consideration,' he replied hurriedly. 'I accept the force of your objections: please think no more of it.'

'If it is any consolation to you, Sir John, I daresay the majority of the men—and my staff—would relish a chance to have a go at the Rooskies. I bid you good-day.'

Sir John turned silently away, and, spurring his wretched horse, rode through the mud towards Balaklava. Despite my anger, I was surprised that I cared so little how he would report our conversation to Lord Raglan: he and his ilk were still deep-rooted in a transport system that was old at the time of the Peninsular War, forty years before. Yet I was somewhat amazed at his rigid attitude, for while I was still only a trainee engineer with Midland Counties, Sir John had been a senior administrator dealing with Irish railway matters. Surely, I thought, he should have learned from that experience? Perhaps, though, what had stuck in his gullet was the very problem he had had to grapple with then, the outright independence of privately-financed railway companies disturbing a regimental mind! His whole life, after all, had been one of public duties diligently pursued though poorly recognised or rewarded, if at all. Little did he—or I, for that matter—dream that in a few brief weeks the War Office would be recalling him.

By the end of the day, with the sky a spectacular grey, but the rain still holding off, our rails were firmly across the new bridge and a good 200 yards beyond. The night air bit to the bone; I warmed myself at a brazier and watched Matt's night-shift stretching the roadbed away towards the flickering lights of the sutlers' camp.

The thought of that burgeoning town was disturbing, and I took a turn up to the gangers' hut at the end of the long line of navvy barracks for a quiet chat with Tom Grace. As I passed along, I caught a glimpse of Barber Bill sitting on a stool, a cape pulled round his thin shoulders. A group of navvies lounged in a doorway as he sang an old ballad, soft and sickly as dripping treacle. Going into Tom's hut I heard sudden shouts and sounds of a scuffle behind me, and Bill's raised voice in warning: 'Break it up, mateys, break it up, or the Provost's men will come and grab you!' There was, I thought grimly, nothing remotely non-combatant about my navvies.

'When they get going like that you can hear 'em down at the harbour,' growled Tom, pushing a mug of coffee towards me across the rough table. He puffed reflectively on his pipe, then burst out: 'Honestly, Mr. Beatty, sir, I don't know what's getting into some of 'em. Worse still, two of the ringleaders are me own Dorset boys.'

'Fishy Haddock, Dick Payling?' I hazarded.

'The very same, and now they're thick as thieves with that Kemp. Twice this week they've made a break for that sutlers' camp; twice I've fetched 'em back—last time with bloodied heads. It's wicked liquor they sell down there, sir, real poison. There'll be more blood spilled, mark my word; Fishy's too free with 'is knife: a regular filleter, you might say, and Black Jack's own brother at that game. Then there's the Provost-Marshal's men round the harbour and in that sutlers' camp day and night.'

'It's a problem all right, Tom,' I agreed, 'and no hiding it either. I'll talk it over with Mr. Campbell tonight. I'll not see us disgraced by a few scallywags.'

I was sitting in my chair thinking over Tom's remarks when Donald came downstairs from the sitting room. 'I'm s-surprised to find you actually here, Jim,' he exclaimed. 'You're mostly out nights as well as days: you'll burn yourself out at this rate; we can't afford you cracking up.' His anxiety was genuine; I think I succeeded in reassuring him. Then I repeated Tom Grace's comments.

Donald listened thoughtfully: 'I agree with Tom,' he said finally. 'There's always the risk of an ugly mood developing; not surprising, when you think of the upheaval everyone's had. After all, this isn't just your average tunnel project somewhere in Derbyshire.' He thought for a moment, then continued: 'We've got to be patient with 'em, Jim—firm but patient. They've hardly settled down yet. Work 'em hard; praise 'em hard: that's my solution. Same with the staff, and it seems to be working.'

'Except for Camidge,' I exclaimed. Donald laughed: 'The odd one out, our Charles—the eternal loner!'

'How in heaven could Betts have saddled us with such a man? He's upsetting everyone—even quarrels with his own cashiers.' I didn't mention the seething restiveness of Jim Lewis, his deputy, or my belief that he was making a real dog's breakfast of my own finances.

Camidge apart, the rest of the staff were turning out a pretty convivial bunch; we were already beginning to have one or two fellows dropping in on us for lunch. It provided a good chance to hear the latest rumour and gossip—yesterday's being that Lord Lucan, commander of the Cavalry Division, was being recalled summarily to England. Fresh faces, with different problems, stopped us getting too absorbed in our own concerns.

But, though I had several times invited them, our two scripture readers had not yet formed part of our happy band of brothers. For parsons, they were surprisingly reserved. George Gyngell, the elder of the two, might have felt he had to display an especially rigid probity on all occasions: he was tall and sanctimonious, with a voice to match—and chronic dyspepsia, or so Albert Howes confided to me. His fellow priest, Thomas Fayres, was the exact opposite in build and temperament, being short and tubby, with a cheerful voice. He openly chafed against the hours he was being forced to spend sorting through the mounds of tracts and religious books with which Mr. Peto had showered them both before departure.

I invited Parson Tom to come and see what his 'parishioners' were doing. To his credit he donned waterproof boots and clumped up and down the line good humouredly for a couple of hours. I promised him a chapel in *Wildfire*'s hold with enough plank benches for a full congregation of a Sunday, confident that *his* voice at least would fill the echoing space with some message of hope.

Still the blessed wind blew from the south-west and, typically, the navvies cried out against their thick clothing, but it was done with a laugh. The sun sailed across the heavens like a giant orange balloon, and the hills to the east were showing new shoots of rank grass. On lower slopes I could see small clumps of crocuses and mauve hyacinths; birds were flying in and out of bushes. Over the eastern hills and beyond the dotted vineyards were the nearest Allied entrenchments—a company of 42nd Foot, flanked by a Marine battery and backed by Turkish troops. Then, reaching right down to the sea, were two detachments of Rifles and a Naval Brigade contingent. On the drying wind came the faint insistent thump of heavy mortars and the continuous crack of rifle fire.

Our drays relished the warmer air. The clop of their great hooves as they trundled wagons along the completed track was a nostalgic sound. As exciting was the ease with which they drew their high-piled loads—all with an unloading gang aloft: it was truly a foretaste of things to come.

I was on my horse early next morning, intent on seeing what progress Donald and Henry were making in their meticulous survey of Frenchman's Hill. Then, while watching our shires stalk ponderously by, I noticed Lord Raglan with only one staff officer, on the rough track opposite me. He called me over. Mounted, I felt for once in some way level with him.

He remarked, speaking as a cavalryman, how greatly he admired our animals. I told him that a further 65 were on their way out on *Norwich*; then we would make giant strides. The C-in-C, who was on his way to welcome Sir George Brown back from sick leave, requested me to accompany him and to point out my 'dispositions'. The syllables had a pleasant antique ring so I took him at his word.

There was no mistaking the keen appraisal in his eyes as he surveyed our railway yard, the roomy stables, our medical huts and the many storage sheds, with the sidings now complete, and spurs running to the Ordnance area and down to our own nearly-completed wharf. I pointed out the long line of navvy huts on the eastern hill above the town, and he was amused when I told him the names with which they had been christened. 'Names are important to people,' he observed. I wondered whether he had Alma and Inkerman in mind, possibly Sebastopol, even. 'I wouldn't be without my old Shedrach,' he said, patting his horse affectionately, 'and my Miss Mary, for faster speed.' He had already met Campbell and Burke that morning on his way down, he said, and would be glad to meet more members of my staff on a later occasion.

I told him that once we had passed Kadikoi and built a storage depot out towards Highland Brigade's camp, I would be on the plateau for several days planning our line north toward the Woronzoff Road, to serve Second Division, Sir George Brown's Light Division and the nearby siege train. Lord Raglan promptly invited me to dine at his headquarters during that visit. He then volunteered a most unusual suggestion: 'It might be helpful for you Mr. Beatty, to have your own railway hut up there in the staff compound, I will talk to Colonel Steele about it.'

'Rags' was a gentleman at heart. If he could only have shown something of this true nature to the troops as he had just done privately to me, the general view of him as an aloof, aristocratic commander might have been radically altered. Yet, at the same time, I had experienced the same sense of frustration that many of his senior colleagues undoubtedly often felt. My pointed comments on the Commissary-General's antiquated methods were parried with a quiet assertion that his staff were looking into all areas needing adjustment. Direct confrontation was not a weapon that could usefully be employed against Lord Raglan: he would deftly turn the edge of contentious argument by a simple statement of fact or a practical observation that was wholly innocuous!

It was clear to me that with such a commander nothing would ever fundamentally change. Army attitudes had become frozen in a kind of historical aspic; everywhere was rigidity, precedence, conformity and insensitivity—how else could a commander of the Light Brigade, Lord Cardigan, continue to live in Balaklava harbour on his private yacht, *Dryad*, complete with French chef? Yet side by side with this congealed conformity there went great gallantry by individual officers, too. I felt myself even more free now to *press forward* in the true spirit of Peto.

We had redoubled our efforts to get the line out well beyond the sutlers' camp, and our horses and men were responding to the continued fine dry weather. Even the enemy seemed to have succumbed to some dream of spring, though experience should have told them that such a spell so early on never lasted in the Chersonese. Their sharpshooters had almost stopped firing at us, and the only major harassment was the constant cloud of flies following our every movement.

Perhaps the Russian general staff—like ours—was living in a past century with no conception of a railway as an operational weapon. Yet, news of what we intended to do had been spelled out plainly back in December, notably in the pages of the *Illustrated London News*. It seemed unlikely that such news had not reached the defenders of Sebastopol. Perhaps something highly unpleasant would be ready to greet us when we came to make our slow way up Frenchman's Hill.

What was concerning me more at present was the threat presented by the sutlers, whose shacks and tents were spreading up the hillside like some vile fungus. The place called up vividly my childhood's picture of Bunyan's 'Vanity Fair'. During the day it looked just that—a tawdry, tenth-rate market-cum-fairground, but at night, with the flares lit, each tent and stall glittered with evil promise; traders vied with each other pushing their wares in every known tongue while in the shadows lurked gaudily-clad whores— grandmothers as well as young girls. Heaven knows where they hid themselves in the day, but, veiled, they probably simply merged into the dense crowds that jostled ceaselessly by. Small wonder that the soldiers lingered round the stalls or that our navvies were all eyes.

The camp was a gigantic free-for-all: the only deterrent was the occasional presence of the Provost-Marshal's men who marched around with ostentatious swords, dressed in fantastical uniform, helmet and red tunic braided with black cord, more suited to a music-hall chorus than any military body. They were new arrivals, few in number, drawn from the Irish constabulary and the Metropolitan police, whose main purpose was reputed to be deterring thieving from cargo ships in the harbour. But from what I witnessed in my journeying up and down the line, they spent most of their time breaking up fights between drunken soldiers and sutlers, and wheeling culprits away for summary flogging.

Not surprisingly, they were detested by the average soldier, not least because of their high scale of pay: James Lewis told me it reached £100 a year—high enough to be taxable!

I thought of warning our men of the dangers they ran in falling foul of the provos and paying the penalty. Talk about 'Parson' Beatty! But there seemed more important things to do: anyway there were few provos about.

Balaklava
16th February 1855

My Ever Dearest Sal

One of the 71st fellows has just come in to tell me there is to be a mail sent off tonight so I'm scribbling a few lines to say we are all tolerably well. For the past few days the weather has been—for once—kind, and the barometer is staying up, which means we have been able to push the work forward with a vengeance. This morning I showed Lord Raglan round our 'dispositions', as he calls them. We had a great jaw and shook hands thrice. I begin to look on general officers as very small fry, and in fact am becoming very cheeky!

I went out the other morning very early with the 71st; there were rumours of an attack on Balaklava, and all troops had been alerted, but it all turned out to be humbug. You have no idea of the lies told here every day; it is perfectly incredible. One day it will be the French having got into Sebastopol; on another, a grand advance by the Russians and an English battery destroyed. But they are all equally false: I never believe anything now unless I see it or meet someone who has seen it...

I have received the books—such a lot! I shall

never have time to read them; it's as much as I can do to get through the papers. You may stop the Daily News *and all railway and other papers—except* The Times. *It is too expensive, and they come in such extraordinary ways that I often get today's papers before those of a week earlier.*

I received a cheque of Campbell's of £36. 15s. 0d. which Mr. Willat will pay into my account at the London First Bank in Princes St. or you can send it to the manager, Mr. Pollard: it is not worth a journey for yourself.

I have received from Steinhauser three cases of wine—viz. one champagne, one port, one sherry and three cases of cordials. The port is very good and I would advise your getting some of the same for yourself. Henry had a slight touch of the blue devils a short time ago but he is quite himself again now; he is working pretty hard, and the others—Kellock etc.— take to him. Camidge is still as bad as ever; no one speaks to him now if they can avoid it. I really think he is mad. It is dreadfully close. The climate is certainly trying but with care I think one may get on very well. I have had one or two touches of gripe from drinking the rum, but a little blue pill always sets me right again—in fact, thank God I am exceedingly well.

This morning I was able to rig up two tubs for myself and Donald by cutting a great pork barrel in two, and we had a cold bath. (Oh, how I would enjoy my old shower-bath and a large sponge!) However, it is very jolly getting a wash at all, and it freshens one up amazingly.

Campbell, Henry and self get on very well together. Donald very kindly proposed that Henry should only pay half the same as we do as his share of the living, but in regard to the drinkables he must pay his third as he takes his full share of those luxuries!

135

A mail is expected in tomorrow. I am dearest Sal so glad to hear news of you and the dear chicks: I do little else but think of you all. The boy must be becoming a screamer, by your account. I trust little Susy will get over her wheezing, etc. Nan-Nan seems to be all right. Kiss the dear little pets for me, and with love to Eliza, believe me, ever dearest wife, your affectionate husband,
James Beatty.

14

OPENING DAY

23rd February

Aided by a drying wind from the west we pressed on to our goal—
Kadikoi—and the formal opening of the line by my target date of
23rd February. This would redeem Mr. Peto's pledge to the Prime
Minister to have the railway working three weeks after the arrival of
the navvies. Once that was reached, his promise of seven miles of
track in seven weeks would be easier to achieve. My determination to
fulfil it had by now become an obsession.

Things seemed to be conspiring in our favour; the air had an
almost spring-like feel. Even the Russian lookouts appeared affected
by it, as though they had lost interest in our proceedings or just didn't
know what to make of them. Anyway, I was glad to be relieved of
their firing, if only temporarily, so as to concentrate on the job in
hand. This unexpected fine spell wouldn't last, of course; even I, as a
newcomer, knew the Chersonese weather was merely mocking us.
The longer it stayed warm, the more pestilence would be sucked up
from the ground; then, typhus and other low fevers would regain their
grip, and the lines of our sick would again lengthen down the
mountain.

I pitied the youngsters who formed the bulk of the new drafts of
troops, now arriving in shoals. Anyone under twenty-five hadn't
enough stamina; they'd go off like shots, as had even veterans before
them. The stories were, I knew, only too true of shattered remnants of
famous regiments being shipped back to Malta to 're-form'. Most of
my staff, thank God, were battling strongly on, their minds totally
absorbed in the daily round. Kellock insisted on doing his full whack,
but I could see that the capricious climate was getting him down
slowly: he was but a shadow of the man who had triumphed over such
savage conditions in New Brunswick. As for myself, I had to admit

reluctantly to occasional spells of lassitude. There was something in
the infernal climate that pulled one about a good deal: I couldn't walk
even five miles with anything like the ease that I could back in
England. Donald's enthusiasm and strength never flagged, though: his
smiling face was a constant tonic to everyone.

Predictably, the military response to its overall parlous straits
was varied: one cavalry officer told me today he was making tentative
plans for a race meeting. Meanwhile, other off-duty sportsmen were
cheerfully risking an occasional Russian shell or round shot to shoot
duck near the Tchernaya—some even using French soldiers as paid
decoys to distract the gunners while they stalked mallard.

The speed at which our work was progressing and the balmy air
had encouraged me to make plans—modest ones—for celebrating
Opening Day of the railway, which Lord Raglan had agreed to attend.
Nothing elaborate *à la* Brunel, with sit-down luncheon for bigwigs
plus champagne and speeches, but nevertheless something distinctive
to fit the occasion. I thought we could rig up a couple of beflagged
wagons for the C-in-C, his generals and personal staff. Captain
Lushington had sportingly volunteered to provide a naval band, and
my good friend Sir Colin Campbell promised to come with his pipers.
This emphasis on music was faintly reminiscent of our grand parade
down the main street at Birkenhead in December when our first party
embarked on *Wildfire*.

All veterans of that epic voyage, including one who had been
summarily flogged only yesterday with a soldier for attempted theft,
were insistent on being present! Personally, I would have liked the
whole of the expedition to have taken part, with a cracking tuck-in
afterwards—and booze, too, but not the abominations sold at Vanity
Fair. But the work could not be halted, not even in a good cause. The
bulk of the men would by then be at least a mile on beyond Kadikoi,
hastily erecting storage sheds at the depot and arranging temporary
navvy hutting and tents for our Croats. From there it would be simple
to supply Highland Brigade with all their stores and with rations, too;
in return, their men would give us a hand up Frenchman's Hill.

The old fogies of generals were at last beginning to see what a
railway could mean, but they were sad old women, most of them. I

wondered how many would actually bother to turn up on the day. Barber Bill had contributed an unexpected mite to the jollifications: he handed me, rather bashfully, some verses he had written. Judging from its first stanza I doubted if it would attain immortality:

> *Hail, th' advance across a hostile plain*
> *Of Albion's all-pow'rful railway track!*
> *Nor snow, nor sleet can halt our gallant band*
> *Whose mighty pow'r will drive th' enemy back!*
> *Then huzza, huzza, hail these dauntless men!*

It was doggerel all right, but it had an honest ring. I told Bill I would show it to the Commander-in-Chief, which more than satisfied our patriotic barber.

John Parker begged to parade all his thirty-five horses, with their drivers. That would have caused too much distraction; he was happy in the end with my suggestion that he pick his eight best animals and have them draw four wagons laden with rails and sleepers past the reviewing party, and then on north of the town to the working gangs at the new depot. At the ceremony we could rely on a large uninvited audience of locals.

Swan came over on his decrepit pony. 'I want to get our gear up to the Col while the going's good,' he said. 'We've got it as far as Frenchman's Hill: two stationary engines, wire rope and the equipment for the artesian wells.' He'd cajoled a bunch of Jacks from Captain Lushington, who acted as though this was a special prank devised for their amusement. I watched with Swan as the bare-footed sailors took a purchase on the ropes and began hauling the loads up the steep track to the Col, 600 feet above. They sang as they heaved, accompanied by a fiddler who danced along beside them. Swan told me later that the whole passage had been observed by several Cossacks on the northern hills. 'They shook their lances at us,' he said, 'but made no move. Just as well, for it was slow work—one-in-seven gradient in places. We'll need our strongest gangs to work that stretch: it seems endless.'

Then, next night, the snow struck; by morning the plain was

inches deep and drifts were piling up against every wagon, driven by a wind now blowing relentlessly from the north-east. The temperature was 14°F: it felt like the end of the known world; everything familiar was reduced to anonymous white. I need not have worried: something of the spirit of the shanty-singing sailors had got into the men: stoical determination carried them through. They could see the dome of Kadikoi's church straight ahead of them; difficulties were brushed aside; Vanity Fair was, by common consent, out of bounds—maybe the lesson of that recent flogging had been taken to heart.

It had certainly taken me by surprise: I only heard of the incident hours later. 'I heard our man,' Donald told me, 'roaring like a bull, though the soldier with him uttered not a sound.' Six of the Provost-Marshal's men seized the couple who were openly making off with a bag of money from a sutlers' stall. 'Twenty-five lashes apiece!' reported Donald. 'It was all over quickly. Afterwards our man, with grog inside him, fancied himself as a hero. "I was flogged for Queen and country," he kept shouting, quite proud of himself.' Donald sounded amused, and everyone who knew Andy Warner, a swarthy, brawling bruiser, agreed he'd had his just come-uppance. I thought of my earlier good intentions; maybe... I confess I felt too tired to think the matter through further.

The snow, solid in the relentless wind, gave us two more days and nights of torment. Vigils with the night shift left me numb. Snow particles slipped through every garment, however tightly belted; each step was a hazard. The men stuck at it heroically, and we reached our goal with a day in hand. Any small spark of triumph, however, was dampened by the sleet that followed the snow and by our over-whelming fatigue. Even Donald, for once, looked exhausted. Yet we were only half way: there was so much still to do.

Opening Day was an anti-climax, but I could hardly blame the weather for that. Overnight, though, the wind had shifted back to the west; now the landscape that met our eyes was the familiar mixture of churned up mud and spreading lakes of melting slush. I had made a saluting base for Lord Raglan from three wagons, positioned on a temporary siding; the flags draping it now hung as wet as tea-towels. Officers, arriving early for the ceremony, climbed grimly aboard and, with expressionless faces, stared at the villagers swarming along the side of the main track. They were kept off the actual rails by a posse of provos, their swords drawn for the occasion. Their presence was watched even more anxiously by the restless stream of eager traders who peddled their bizarre wares in all the languages of the Middle East.

Standing out in this motley crowd was Mrs. Seacole, the Creole lady from Jamaica, in a bright yellow dress, coloured shawl and a simple straw wide-awake with gay red streamers. I had known her since my first days in Balaklava: she used to camp out on a wharf, selling goods from a tarpaulined store and helping to shift the wounded from mules and carts into ships for Scutari. 'I nursed Lord Nelson's godson back from yellow fever—and then married him,' she told me once with pride. 'I nursed many young naval officers in Jamaica, including Admiral Boxer's son. He was a young man then.'

She told me she was now building a hotel with her cousin, a few hundred yards from our Kadikoi depot. 'I'm going to call it Spring Hill,' she said. 'For comfort and convenience of English officers. I'm a cook as well as a good nurse,' she added with her flashing smile. 'I hope, sir, I may enjoy your custom and that of your staff.' Given the setting, it all seemed like a fairy tale.

From the crowd an unknown officer hailed me gruffly: 'Mr. Beatty, I'm Munro of the 39th. Sam Park told me about you. Thought I'd come and greet you. You'll be sorry to hear that Sam was killed two days ago—on reconnaissance, shot clean through the head by a sniper. A good man!' What a moment to hear such news of a true friend.

It was a relief to turn to the business of the day. Lord Raglan, in dress uniform and plumed headgear, arrived punctually from Balaklava. He was accompanied by a Lord George Paget, just landed from *Australian*, the town commandant and Captain Heath. Two other naval captains also showed up—Lushington and Peel. The C-in-C, though polite to me, appeared abstracted, as though the unscheduled appearance of Lord George had in some manner put him out. He was curt with Sir John Burgoyne who looked uncomfortable and faintly ridiculous in uncongenial surroundings.

Any pretence of conversation faded as the Highland pipers struck up, backed by drums and bugles of the naval brigade band. Then, led by a beaming John Parker, our first drays stalked majestically past, each pair decked with different-coloured ribbons, all brasses agleam and harness bright as a guardsman's boots. What caught everyone's imagination was the rumble of the four heavy wagons they were drawing—each loaded high, with navvies aloft. The crowd roared at the spectacle. As a mischievous tailpiece came one last truck, piled even higher, with commissariat rations for the Highland Brigade. Out of the corner of my eye I caught a quick grin on Sir Colin Campbell's face. Needless to say, Mr. Filder, though invited personally by me, had chosen to absent himself.

But no speech was made: indeed, after a perfunctory drink with me and some of my staff, Lord Raglan and his party rode off in silence to headquarters. I was not sorry; only sad that they had not risen to the occasion. Lord Raglan's reticence must, I thought, spring from some innate awkwardness when faced with a public appearance, particularly one not under his control. His illustrious chief, the Duke of Wellington, would have conjured something symbolic and inspiring out of the occasion. As for the French emperor... he would have distributed medals and bottles of cognac to all concerned!

Our navvies certainly seized their brief moment to eat and drink in customary style. Their daily four tots of issue rum in lieu of their preferred Barclay and Perkins Entire gave them a keen appetite for mid-day vittals, which they shared spontaneously with some of our Croats and a few lucky bystanders.

That afternoon Kellock showed me the general layout and proposed sidings of the Kadikoi depot. They were all coming along as planned, but I left with a nagging conviction that we would need more sidings and certainly more sheds if we were ever going to reduce clutter on the quayside at Balaklava. I decided also to enlarge the temporary camp for our Croats.

Henry and Tom Grace were keeping the working shift at a pace that had our time-keepers at full stretch, but I wanted to cross this last level section much faster: the dry west wind was a dangerous illusion—by tonight all could easily turn to snow again. Henry went back to mobilise a second gang of navvies and Croats, while I traversed the route forward on foot, past 4-gun Battery and on around Frenchman's Hill. Every muddy step sapped my energy; even the freshening wind couldn't blow away an insidious listlessness.

I suppose I could have kept my horse, one of the two Henry had bought so triumphantly. But we were forced to lay them up for lack of fodder, and, by a bit of luck, had managed to sell them at a slight profit. On the whole I was glad to be rid of them; I certainly hadn't come out to the Crimea to become a dealer in horseflesh. Like any infantryman, mine was basically a foot-slogging job, though I wasn't confined to trenches night and day and could always get a lift to my quarters on one of our wagons. So, the nearer the ground the better for our purposes, I felt; that, and *Press forward.*

Donald, down from the Col, reported new activity by Russian troops on Canrobert's Hill. 'They've not put any guns there yet, Jim,' he said, 'but a few shells exploding among the rocks could cause us casualties higher up. We'll have to limit night work, I'm afraid, unless there's a moon: our flares would offer too tempting a target. I don't suppose the C-in-C would consider some kind of a sortie, as a diversion?' I shook my head: a night operation of that kind was not to the taste of a soldier like Lord Raglan.

On our way back we passed Mrs. Seacole supervising work on her hotel site up the slope. 'We'll be ready next month,' she called down. 'Then there'll be a grand opening!' One had to admire her spirit.

Balaklava
23rd February 1855

My ever dearest Wife
This is the opening day of the railway and we are sending up a lot of things for the Army: I hope it will be of use to them. Today has been mild and pleasant and we are sitting with the windows open, but this is tempting fate and I don't encourage it. My head is giddy with the noise of men and animals in the street outside—and camp followers of every description! I

143

*haven't told you before about the womankind out here.
There is a Mrs. Duberley, who lives on* Star of the East.
*She is the wife of the paymaster of Eighth Hussars, and
sees everything that is going on. She rode on the field
of Inkerman after the battle: in England she is what we
should term a strong-minded woman! Then there is
another of the same kidney, a Mrs. Major Lyster, who
drinks a trifle. A few captains of transports have their
wives out here, but they live on board ship and do not
show themselves much. There are also a few soldiers'
wives—that's all the female fraternity out here. Any
man who would subject his wife to the annoyance, filth
and frustration of this place must be mad or have very
little respect for her.*

*Colonel Ridley and his regiment have come down
to Balaklava: he told me they have got just 146 men
fit for duty out of 1,300. I hope that with the arrival
of the railway the state of the army will be improved
in a short time.*

*I have not heard from you for the last ten days,
and cannot understand it, I suspect it is all the fault
of the Post Office. I trust, my dearest wife, that you
are quite well, and the little ones also.*

> *2nd March*

*I received your letter of 12th yesterday and am
astonished that you had not heard from me: I have
written every mail since I arrived at Balaklava, and
you should have received my first about the 3rd or
4th of February. However I am glad to hear you and
the dear children are well—the weather seems to be
much more severe with you in London than it is in
the Crimea! We have some very cold days
occasionally but they do not last: the weather has
been oppressive for the last week but tonight it is
intensely cold.*

I am DV off to the front tomorrow to set out the line ahead. I shall have to sleep under canvas, but that is nothing. I hope to leave Balaklava shortly for higher ground: this is a putrid charnel house. Thousands have been buried within a mile of the place since the war commenced; the poor Turks particularly have gone the way of all flesh pretty steadily. All the fellows do very well except Camidge. He is a thundering fool, and I fear we shall have to get rid of him.

I fear my letters from here are very stupid things. I really feel it impossible to write, the infernal noise in all directions would confuse a saint. I see Mr. Peto is to be made a Baronet—he deserves it and I am glad of it. I shall offer him my congratulations. I write to you twice every week. Kiss the dear chicks.

Camidge continued to behave like a madman, quarrelling with everybody. He had made a dead set at Filder: our Commissary-General might have met his match at last. Unfortunately, this only made Filder more intransigent, and he identified me as the real troublemaker. In consequence, he put every obstacle in my path and foiled all my efforts to persuade him to use the railway even as far as Kadikoi. It took me three days to squeeze 200 commissariat mules out of him to take stores forward to the Highland Brigade camp. Once there the soldiers got them—one way or another—up to the terminus on the plateau. But a couple of medium-sized shells were quite enough to exhaust even the most dogged mule.

Henry volunteered to come to the front with me; very handsome of him, considering the amount of time he had spent up there recently with Donald. He got hold of two mules and collected our tent and gear, including storm-wear and extra long boots, so that we could get away at first light. The temperature was down to 24°F and the ground was hardening by the minute; fortunately, the snow held off. We got the tent up without mishap, and put in two good days surveying the last sections of the line. This was to run as far as the

Woronzoff Road, to serve the Second and Light Divisions, with a branch winding round the rear of Cathcart's Hill to a spot between the Third and Fourth Divisions.

Immediately I was invited to dine with Lord Raglan. Henry being more than happy to be carried off by an Irish acquaintance to enjoy a regimental occasion, I walked down the path to headquarters with mixed feelings, chiefly a sense of frustration at having to leave that day's survey calculations unfinished. I was definitely in no mood for polite conversation—or for gossiping, for that matter. However, that thought pulled me up: perhaps this invitation might reveal a silver lining, as had my unusual encounter with Lord Stratford. I owed it to the expedition I was leading to play the part...

Lord Raglan's farmhouse was a more substantial structure than I had imagined it from the outside, tucked into a hollow, facing down a ravine towards Sebastopol harbour. Its size was masked by the many buildings and tents surrounding it on three sides. Here were housed the Adjutant-General's office and huts for Dr. Bell, the principal medical officer, and Colonel Blane, the commandant. There were huts, too, for General Simpson and General Estcourt, and also for Lord Burghersh and the other ADCs—Kingscote and Calthorpe. Detachments of Eighth Hussars and First Royals guarded the camp; the C-in-C had his own personal Dragoon escort. As I found out later, the compound contained marquees, a Church hut, a medical room, a post office, extensive stabling, a commissariat yard, two water wells—and three vineyards.

The C-in-C's dwelling seemed dark and positively stuffy. To the right of the long hall in the north wing was the room of the French liaison officer, Colonel Vico (with a hen-house outside his window), then came a pantry. Beyond, was Sir John Burgoyne's combined office and bedroom. The Military Secretary informed me he would shortly be leaving for England on recall and that his position as senior engineer adviser was to be taken by a Major-General Jones, 'a very active man.' I hoped he would prove as much. Anyway, by the time he had settled in, our line should have been almost completed.

Ahead lay Lord Raglan's dining room which opened out of his simple office with its writing table, camp bed in a corner, clothes racks and a small dressing table under the west window. Adjacent was the room of General Airey, the Quartermaster-General. Incongruously, the next room was a winter biscuit store for the troops. Odder still, a cow was kept in the cellar under Dr. Prendegast's room. Near at hand were the bedrooms of Colonel Somerset and Colonel Steele.

Before dinner the ADCs were politely concerned to make me feel at home. Sherry—exceedingly good sherry—circulated, and I was quizzed in interested tones not so much about my current activities as on my own personal background. None of these pleasant young men had served in Canada, but two had been stationed in Dublin and were loud in recollections of hunts followed and carefree days at the Curragh. There was no sense of military purpose about them; their private concerns were identical with those of the other serving officers I was meeting daily—the high cost of purchasing promotion; conventional aristocratic social chit-chat. Having greeted me civilly, Lord Raglan retired to a corner to discuss a dispatch with his military secretary.

The kitchen had been erected close to the farm-house, but there was no question of food being served lukewarm. All arrangements were in the hands of an upper servant called Ferdinand—a German, I was informed, who spoke perfect English and French and had an engagingly obliging manner. Though nominally the C-in-C's valet, attending to his personal wants, brushing his clothes and boots etc., he also regulated his table, acting exactly as a butler in a nobleman's family in England.

The C-in-C sat halfway down the long table, I was placed at his left hand; on his right was his nephew, charged with cutting up the viands on his plate. The mutton was exceedingly tender, and the vegetables unbelievably fresh. As for the wines—they certainly weren't bought at any sutler's stall! I found out later that they came from Constantinople along with all other provisions ordered weekly by the French chef.

I noticed that Lord Raglan gave more attention to the food than to those around the table; more, I concluded, from an habitual reserve than greediness—in fact, he ate very little and drank even less. Fortunately I found a talkative neighbour in a Mr. Calvert, who had been for many years our consul at Gallipoli and was now an adviser on Russian matters at HQ. He was fluent in the language, having acquired a Russian wife while serving in the St. Petersburg embassy, and hinted that he had tried—unsuccessfully—to persuade Lord Raglan to let him set up an unofficial spy service. I wasn't wholly convinced he was telling the truth but was unable to press him on the matter as dinner concluded and my host turned to me.

He remarked that Sir Colin Campbell had warmly praised the railway to him for bringing up hutting and stores so speedily to his camp; he himself had been struck by the huge loads our cart horses were able to pull effortlessly; nothing the artillery horses nor commissariat mules could carry was comparable, and even those loads took toll of the animals. Without questioning directly, Lord Raglan seemed to be probing for my view about future developments: I stated outright that I would be getting supplies and ammunition up to the divisional camps by 26th March—despite all obstacles in our path. That remark was quietly ignored! However, the C-in-C looked pleased, though slightly incredulous. 'We will do it despite the weather, sir,' I declared. 'That was what Mr. Peto pledged to Lord Aberdeen: "Seven miles of railway in seven weeks".' 'Well and good,' was Lord Raglan's response. 'Please repeat that to Colonel Steele.'

Everyone got up, and I went over to buttonhole the Military Secretary, but he forestalled me by remarking that the C-in-C had written to the Duke of Newcastle praising the railway's speedy progress. This encouraged me, and I decided to broach the prickly topic of Mr. Filder, my adversary-in-chief. 'He wears me out, too,' he confessed. 'Nearly three-quarters of the complaints I get concern his department, but even burning all his regulations wouldn't solve the problem: Filder knows them by heart! However, things are improving, thanks to you, Beatty. We'll soon be getting a cargo of warehouse buildings from home, complete with warehousemen: that should bring some welcome order into commissariat matters.'

At the other end of the room Lord Raglan sat, surrounded by his staff, an enigmatic figure, silent but solidly himself. Was he brooding perhaps on the problems of handling the Allied generals, of having to treat with Admiral Dundas as with an equal in command of the campaign? His ADCs had told me privately of their concern at the long hours he spent at his desk each day—and often far into the night—composing elegant replies to dispatches from the Secretary of State for War. I well understood how exhausting such tasks were. Soon the arrival of the electric telegraph would enmesh him still further in the War Office web! The cable-laying vessel had just been reported two-thirds of the way across the Black Sea, to make landfall at St. George's monastery.

My reflections were broken by a Scots voice: 'My staff tell me, Mr. Beatty, that you were surveying near my lines this afternoon.' The speaker was Sir George Brown. 'What, pray, are you about?'

I explained it was for a branch line to serve his division. He gave me a considering appraisal: 'How soon, sir, will I start getting my supplies?'

'By the 26th of this month.'

'Is that a promise?'

'Yes, sir.'

'Good, I like someone who knows his mind.' Sir George was famous for knowing his. He faced me foursquare, clean-shaven, in immaculate uniform that fitted perfectly, tight stock in place as always, summer and winter. A brave and generous man, though medically short-sighted, as were many of his senior contemporaries. I could well believe the story told of him during the Inkerman battle when he had risen from a sickbed to take charge. Finding his second-in-command firmly in control he stayed on as aide-de-camp to let him win his spurs.

I was invited again to dine at HQ the next evening, this time by Lord Raglan himself who walked down to my tent personally. The dinner was absolutely ambrosial! Afterwards, he offered me a cigar. He didn't smoke one himself but looked on complacently. His first remark took my breath away: 'I've talked with Steele about your railway hut,' he said. 'Would you find it helpful to have one here in the compound? We're putting one up for the electric telegraph next to the post office, and yours could be alongside.'

I accepted his offer with alacrity: it would be invaluable. Lord

Raglan looked pleased; 'You'll get the latest news, even before I do—and the gossip, too,' he added with a smile.

Another example of the C-in-C's thoughtfulness was told me by Nigel Kingscote. A corporal's wife had given birth to a baby in last month's snow in a dog kennel tent, about four miles from HQ. The tent was nothing but a pit dug in the frozen earth with wooden hoops covered by a waterproof cap. Hearing of this, Lord Raglan had taken her some milk and a bottle of brandy and water, a waterproof sheet and a blanket. He later returned to see how she was getting on, with little comforts from his kitchen.

Henry and I were dismantling our tent when fierce firing broke out between the Russian and French lines, the sound of musketry mingling with the deafening roar of cannonades. Some Russian move was obviously threatening; as we picked our way down the incline we could see the French 9th Division moving up towards the Victoria Redoubt.

But other divisions, too, were afoot: the first spring meeting opened on undulating ground on the ridge tops near Karanyi—dog hunting, to start with! Even if the local curs didn't relish having to run for their lives, it tickled officers and men alike. It also caught the attention of Cossack piquets at Kamara, and a party of twelve horsemen approached our vedette at No. 4 Old Redoubt in the valley. Fired on by the Dragoons they fled, but two were captured, both of them Polish officers.

We got down Frenchman's Hill safely, but immediately ran headlong into a crisis in our own ranks. Tom Grace broke the news: 'Same trouble as before, Mr. Beatty. Three of 'em 'ad a skinful of rum last night and slipped off to Vanity Fair to get more. They roughed up one of the provos, really mashed 'im—fighting drunk they was. In the end Mr. Campbell managed to square the Provost-Marshal hisself or they'd all be under close arrest by now. Our chaps got an almighty flogging—no 'arf measures. Pity is, sir, they're three of my own Dorchester lads.'

'Which three?'

'Dick Payling, Borthwick, Daddy Williams—on my oath, the last three I'd ever 'ave expected.'

'Old Daddy—I can't believe it! Well, they'll go back to England on the next steamer: I'll tell them so myself. They're to be aboard a ship this very night, Tom. As for the rest of the men, tell them tomorrow morning—anyone causing mischief like that again and they'll be flogged and sent home in disgrace.'

'Right Mr. Beatty—no more junketing, I vote, till the line's finished right to the top—'

'—*and* double-tracked from Balaklava to Kadikoi, *and* a branch built to Diamond Wharf, Tom. Then'll be the time to relax.'

I called in the whole staff for a talk that evening, and thanked Donald for his intervention. 'They c-came damn close to a court martial,' he said, 'though technically they're civilians, as we all are.'

'Deuced difficult to argue that case in the heat of the moment, Donald. We must just somehow get into their thick skulls what will happen if they go on in this way.'

Judging from the silence when I had finished, they seemed to take my warning to heart, though I still had reservations about some of the men—Black Jack Kemp, Fishy and others of their kidney. But the weather was on our side: day after day Donald and Henry led the men storming up the hill. I'd managed to keep our Jacks for a longer spell, and they pitched in with gusto. Having the navvy huts at the new depot, with Croats alongside, cut travelling time and gave a fillip to the work. Our track was now fully five miles long.

A bonus was the clear sky filled with eagles, buzzards and kites; larks, finches and wagtails flew around us. Even the murky waters at the head of the harbour had their resident cormorants, divers and widgeon, along with other waterfowl I'd never seen before.

Most evenings, the French camps resounded to drum rolls and bugle calls repeated endlessly, but in our lines there had been no regimental music for months. Barber Bill filled the gap for us with impromptu sing-songs held near the huts after supper. It was a heartening sight to see navvies sitting on sleepers listening intently, pipes alight, as he sang *Willikens and his Dinah* as though his life depended on it. The choruses were roared out full-throatedly, carrying far across the plain in the still air.

I set Kellock and Wright to laying the double track from Balaklava to the new depot, and took over supervision of the new half-mile branch to Diamond Wharf myself. Swan and his miners, working with army sappers, had blasted tons of rock from the cliffs close to the water; this was dragged away by our Croats and tipped into the fever swamp at the head of the harbour. At the seaward end we planned a jetty which could handle the largest vessels.

With each extension of the line we were capable of sending greater quantities of stores forward, along with our normal construction loads, but this involved a never-ending tussle with Filder and his tight-fisted staff. Army rations, they insisted, could only be applied for and collected from the main commissariat store. I was incensed at their continuation of peacetime working practices—an 8 am start, with a very prompt finish at 5.30 pm irrespective of traffic demands.

I had to explain all this as patiently as I could to a new colleague who had just arrived. He was Colonel William McMurdo, just appointed, as he informed me, by the Duke of Newcastle to head up the newly-formed Land Transport Corps, under my direction. Once all lines were completed, this body was to assume responsibility for running the railway operationally. A first contingent of 300 recruits was to join him from England. He himself, he told me, was an Indian Army man. I thought it prudent to tell him something of Mr. Filder's temperament before I introduced them. After their brief discussion a new McMurdo emerged—fiery, almost spitting blood. 'Nothing but an infernal box-wallah,' he fumed, 'skin like a rhino!' I promised to talk more with him later; but he left me in a state of agitation.

Our big day now arrived: the railway, completed as far as HQ, opened officially on 26th March! Lord Raglan came down to Balaklava to witness the start, travelling in a wagon I had had rigged up specially with a canvas roof, for fear of sudden snow. The day turned out to be the hottest of the year! The occasion went well— much better than the Kadikoi exercise—though celebrations were somewhat muted by news of heavy French losses the night before during a fierce battle in the rifle pits. Donald and I were introduced to Major-General Jones, who looked everywhere about him with interest.

The C-in-C spoke briefly of the railway as 'the new weapon in our armoury,' and gravely watched the first through-train rumble away from the terminus, to the cheers of our assembled navvies. I gave Lord Raglan Barber Bill's verses which Henry Stone had copied out on good cartridge paper and embellished with coloured sketches of navvies on the job. He seemed to find it diverting, then quietly told me he would have to leave, having promised to attend the Third Division races set for that afternoon. He would, however, without fail be at the HQ depot to witness the unloading. Thus he departed, on Miss Mary, his lively mare.

General Jones insisted on seeing everything, so I had no chance—except in imagination—to follow the long line of our wagons on their journey westwards up to the Col. Kellock and Swan were in charge of that crucial stage, but we had had a faultless dress rehearsal for the operation. However, as I knew from experience, anything could go wrong on the great occasion—especially when under the eyes of the Allied Commander-in-Chief and his critical personal staff!

On the trial run twelve fully-laden wagons, each drawn by an immaculate pair of matching drays, reached our Kadikoi depot without incident; once there they were marshalled on a siding and coupled together forming a complete train. This was then coupled to a tender attached to a wire rope carried on rollers positioned between the rails. Then the whole train was pulled steadily up the steep incline by the stationary engine at the top. I privately reckoned that the engine and winding gear could deal with far larger loads, but prudence suggested that we limit the wagon total for the first operational run.

The wagons themselves anyway were a very mixed bunch, both in capacity and shape. They had come from a variety of home railway company lines—some were awkward steep-sided trucks, though admirable for big loads; others were flat-bedded, handy for carrying rails, sleepers and hut sections. Because of their diversity of design there was always a difficulty matching buffer heights and couplings. For short distances on the level, this was not too much of a problem, but particular care had to be taken when assembling a long train for the incline—a disconnection at that critical stage would have been disastrous, especially as we were now being required to transport the heaviest shells and solid shot as well as other supplies.

On opening day, thank goodness, everything went according to plan. John Parker went up to the stationary engines with the first train and supervised the uncoupling of the wagons from the tender. They were taken individually by further pairs of drays up the slight incline to the Col and on to our new depot at HQ. John had stabled his animals snugly on the plateau, and their coats and brasses shone in the unexpected sunshine: it was a highly professional performance on his part and drew admiring comments from even our own hardened engineers.

Tom Grace had relaxed the gangers' iron rule on 'junketing' for this one occasion: the navvies were enjoying a slap-up meal which included a couple of barrels of Barclay and Perkins Entire bought from a transport purser and—wonder of wonders—beefsteaks of giant size. These, I heard later, came fresh from a couple of bullocks (much prized by General Bosquet) which had been found 'straying' by some of our more buccaneering men, and promptly knocked off.

McMurdo wasn't the only perplexed newcomer washed up on Balaklava's shores. Late that night I met another—a Mr. Alfred Pratt, a Customs officer, who had arrived from England to superintend the warehousing and landing of stores. He told me dolefully that no one in authority would give him any duties; his foreman of works, eight warehousemen and the thirty labourers he had brought were just kicking their heels. 'I offered to build a wharf for my warehouses— I'm an engineer,' he said, 'but I couldn't get a site. Now I'm supervising the levelling of a piece of waste ground for hutting—on the princely pay of twenty-five shillings per month.' I felt for that luckless man, but thanked heaven for our own independence.

Donald returned late from HQ. 'I free-wheeled all the way down from the Col to Kadikoi in one of our wagons, with just one brakesman,' he announced with a huge chuckle. 'A t-terrifying ride, but quick! You must try it, Jim.' The unloading went off perfectly said that imperturbable man: Lord Raglan and his staff were impressed—apparently the divisional horse-races had been a success, too. So that was all right: a perfect end to a perfect day!

Balaklava
26th March

My Ever Dearest Wife
The railway was officially opened today... We took up an immense quantity of powder and ball, etc., to the front. There is talk of commencing the bombardment again soon. The Emperor of Russia is reported dead. Heaven knows how it will all end. We shall take Sebastopol, I believe, but I fancy the bulk of the army would prefer to be at home again.

I have been very well, thank God, considering one feels frightfully weak here and loath to make any exertion. A hot sirocco wind has been blowing the last few days and one is almost smothered. The house I live in swarms with fleas and bugs: wasps and hornets are also coming out quite strong!

William Ayling has been laid up for a few days but the doctors tell me he will be out again directly: there is a low fever about that prostrates one for a while, but it is not dangerous. Robert has attended on me during his brother's illness. Dr. Howes has been very ill for the past fortnight and only just now able to sit up: I like him very well. His assistants, too, are able men and understand their profession thoroughly.

The works are going very well, but some of the men have turned out infernal scamps. I am sending home a few of the incorrigibles but will keep the others to see how they get on. It is just possible that they may come bothering you. Do not hold any communication with them; send them back to Peto and Betts' office. We had an unfortunate accident the other day: two men were killed—one a navvy, the other a Spanish muleteer. It was quite accidental, entirely due to want of nerve in our man: they were both completely crushed. I hear he has left a wife and child; we are going to get up a subscription for him. This is only the second man we have lost since we came out, and that was accidental too—a fall down a hatchway on board ship.

The people in England know very little of the nature of this country, nor the extent of ground covered by the British army. The country was once all trees and vines; now it is like a dried-up ploughed field—not a shrub or tree of any description.

On St. Patrick's Day I walked with Ethelbert Blake on the field of Inkerman! Such a sight: dead horses in dozens; old pouches, belts and coats scattered about in all directions. I was not able to pick up a single thing worth bringing home except a button off a Russian coat. There were lots of dead Russians still unburied, but outside our lines.

I have been making a calculation!! and I make out that your little affair cannot come off before 14th May at soonest. So you will be quite safe in having your nurse with you by the end of April, though I am sorry it is not Mrs. Frampton. I am glad Dr. Clarke is to attend you in your confinement. I fear it will be all over before I get home but never mind, you have had some little experience in such matters! Give Eliza my love and tell her that I consider her a brick and a half. I was very much frightened to hear that Nan-Nan had a turn, and trust in God that she is well long ere this. The dear chicks are a source of great anxiety to me and you yourself are hardly ever out of my thoughts.

I must write dispatches now for PB&B: they abuse me for not letting them have detail enough, so I'm going to spin a long jaw for them by this mail— Goodnight; kiss the dear chicks for me.

PS. You might as well pay the enclosed bill.

15

SUCCESS AND A SPILL

7ᵗʰ April 1855

April Fools Day caught us all out with a snowstorm, leaving a legacy of freezing air that the wind turned into torture. But for once the army had reason to rejoice—the growing weight of munitions reaching the front daily since our line opened on 26th March. I wrote privately to Sir Morton Peto to tell him we had redeemed his pledge to the Prime Minister. The expedition had indeed 'pressed forward': the railway had been totally vindicated.

I set the men to completing the final stretches of track to Second Division. This section was under constant threat of Russian fire, but Jack Kemp's gang seemed oblivious of any danger and treated rifle shots as lightly as passing mosquitoes. Even the occasional ball only evoked a shout of 'Wait till we get a gun!' Since our first meeting in Waterloo Road, Kemp had kept his distance from me and also from Tom Grace and the other gangers. His off-duty hours were spent drinking heavily with cronies in his gang who were prepared to put up with his rough moods. Now they were doing a first-class job in dangerous conditions. I told him that when the stretch was finished, he and the men could have a couple of days off at the Kadikoi camp as a reward. His response was a surly request for me to 'make it three'. My face must have indicated the strength of my feeling of disgust at the request: he touched a finger to his cap and turned back to the work without a word.

Conscious of the eye of authority on them, the navvies were, on the whole, displaying their most attractive ways and were winning plaudits on all sides. But the prime favourites were our patient, indomitable drays, smoothly hauling their gigantic loads. One could almost dare to dream that a Golden Age was dawning—but one knew better. Only two nights before, our Croats shattered my picture of harmony with an ugly outburst of quarrelling in their Kadikoi lines. They seemed to feel they were second-class citizens in comparison to the navvies; fortunately, they were disarmed before serious blood was shed. We should probably have taken their knives away before, though they made productive use of them when in the right humour.

The Russians had suddenly become active right along the front. On one occasion their gunners even took exception to smoke from two of my newly-built kilns in the quarry behind Chapman's Battery. They lobbed quite a few shells into it, luckily without causing damage; but our masons started clamouring for a chance to retaliate. Russian troops one night surprised a French working party and a bloody skirmish took place, both sides using their spades, pickaxes and hatchets. Supports were called up, and finally the enemy was repulsed. The Russians lost 150 men, the French 37. Small actions like this rarely got reported.

Artillery duels were now taking place, almost to a pattern, it seemed. When Russian gunners started firing on our positions from new batteries high on the Mamelon, there would be an immediate response from our naval mortars: they went off with a roar that shook the earth and raised tall plumes of dust and debris. Promptly at noon each day, the Russian guns would fall silent, for a meal break; our gunners would follow suit. Then, in later afternoon, both sides would start up again, the firing often continuing far into the night. Those 13-inch mortars of ours were real monsters; yesterday we brought up three, along with quantities of shot and shell, and umpteen barrels of gun powder.

With so many operations to oversee, I now had to divide my time between HQ and Balaklava. Albert Howes' notion of a portable medical hut of our own sited on the plateau had worked extremely well, though, due to his illness, the job had to be carried through by Mike Read, one of his assistant surgeons. It gave immediate aid to those injured on the arduous incline work, and—later—on the final extensions to the front itself. Our doctors had often expressed their contempt for army medical practices and standards of care, and those thoughts came back to trouble me every time I witnessed the columns of sick and wounded soldiers setting out on their way to the hospital above Balaklava or to the steamers for Scutari.

Now at last, I realised, we had an answer to this never-ending ordeal of pain: *we could take them down in our empty wagons—right to the quayside*. I put this proposal at once to Lord Raglan, who gave his assent to the experiment. More surprising, I carried the day with his chief medical officer, too. So I instantly sent a message to Read to organise the first train-load. When I passed the railhead later, the wagons were already half-filled with patients being settled down by a handful of old army medical orderlies co-opted by Read. Propped up on their knapsacks, the men were made as comfortable as possible. Read took charge of the journey down, and reported that it had gone satisfactorily—the time from HQ to sick wharf had been less than an hour! Three of our nurses, led by Mrs. Williamson, had helped the patients embark on the long voyage to Scutari. I vowed to make a hospital train part of our daily pattern.

We had, so far, been tolerably fortunate with sickness among our own men, but Albert Howes' fever made me think more carefully about my staff, as well. From the outset, I had deliberately pared their numbers to the bone, and we could ill afford to see that small total dwindle further. Strangely, both our parsons appeared peaky—the older, Rev. Gyngall, tall and thin, with a mournful manner which did not endear him to the men, looked as though the merest gust of wind might blow him away. Thomas Fayres, his colleague, was the exact antithesis, being fat and jolly, but he was the one who had just gone down with Crimea fever, along with Howes.

It seemed unfair after all his sterling effort. On Palm Sunday he had acquitted himself well, attracting a surprisingly large con-gregation of men, gangers, doctors and nurses. I attended his service with Donald, Henry and two of our time-keepers. I was glad to have kept my promise to Fayres; *Wildfire*'s empty hold was now well fitted up with temporary benches. One of the carpenters, a Methodist, had made a very adequate Cross: candles partly relieved the gloom. Barber Bill, with voice and accordion, and a Gosport fiddler from HMS *Vesuvius*, soon had the men singing hymns they probably hadn't thought about since childhood.

159

The Gospel passage of Jesus entering Jerusalem on a mule got an instant reaction and broad smiles of recognition. Fayres, in clean white surplice, had a resonant voice; his sermon, picturing in simple words the events of Holy Week, echoed round the creosoted beams of the hold with a fine solemnity, and made a singular impression. He even took a collection 'for our less fortunate brothers'. I could see, though, that the effort had drained him; I was not surprised to find him that night in one of our hospital beds, being given a draught by the nurse on duty.

After the service, some navvies strolled along the quayside, smoking pipes and showing off in their finery, content just to observe the tangled mass of shipping from half across the world that clogged the harbour and which our friend, Captain Heath, now re-named Agent of Transports, was striving to reduce to some sort of order. Others of the men were making off hot foot to Vanity Fair, to sample its varied attractions—if not the wine, then the women, some of whom had an undeniable allure, inherited, perhaps, from piratical ancestors!

Indeed, one young minx had tried more than once to catch *my* eye—just as well I was happily married, with three children, and another on the way!

On impulse, I invited McMurdo to dine with us that evening: it would be my last in Balaklava for a few days. I had promised to be at HQ on Good Friday. Lord Raglan had ordered 300 men of the 71st up on mules, to dig advanced trenches and, as an experiment, he wanted them returned to their camp the following day by train. Kellock was organising the necessary sets of wagons but I was keen to take part in the exercise myself: this would be the first time such a large-scale troop movement had been carried out, but after the successful run of the hospital train I felt confident in the outcome. It would give me time beforehand, too, to write a dispatch to Peto & Co.

It was important that McMurdo should understand our methods of working, and the sooner the better, so I took him on a detailed tour of our various establishments. My painstaking explanation of the stores' checking system was drowned by an outburst of bellowing. It came from a steamer just starting to unload.

A succession of these unusual transports had been docking for a week or more, each crammed with wild cattle for food. Used to the Asian hillsides where they had been trapped, these latest arrivals were obviously overcome at being on land again. They broke loose in a frenzy, careered blindly across the wharf and charged headlong down the alleys of Balaklava, butting everything in their way. A Provost-Marshal's man fired at one maddened bull as it passed: his bullet missed and hit a fleeing soldier in the leg. It took a regular fusillade and sundry bayonet lunges to end that beast's frantic dash for freedom.

I found myself warming to Willie McMurdo, partly perhaps because he was only slightly older than me and also because he highly approved of our new hospital train service and vowed to continue it faithfully. His businesslike approach to administrative matters was reassuring; it was certainly unexpected in an officer who had seen action in the Scinde and the North-West Frontier campaigns, before being retired on half pay. In fact, when the summons had come to an appointment in the Crimea he was marking time as assistant adjutant-general at Dublin Castle. This had, no doubt, confirmed his dislike of form-filling and box-wallahs in particular.

'I shall have much to learn from your doctors,' he confided, after I had shown him our medical huts. 'Would you believe, in my first batch of three hundred recruits, sixty-five were suffering from the most civilised clap to be found in Bristol!?' They were due to arrive any day, he said: 'The literal sweepings of our great cities. I doubt if half have ever handled a horse, let alone any tools.'

I urged on him the importance of keeping them fit, well-fed and hard worked—idleness tended to encourage fever, especially among youngsters—and offered him the loan of an engineer and a couple of our toughest gangers to lick them into shape. Later that afternoon, Henry volunteered to take him up the line and point out stretches where his men might expect hazards, for example where track had initially been laid directly on the ground. McMurdo greatly wished to see our stationary engines. I said I would ask Swan to show him one in action and explain its working; he could try out for himself the wagon brakes on the lower slope of the line by the French camp.

161

'Master' Russell arrived in good time as our second dinner guest, and immediately made himself at home. He was a most imposing figure with a thick black beard and a never-ending fund of stories and rollicking songs which made him a good companion in many an officers' mess. Both he and I were Irish and shared the same year of birth, he remarked; he had been born in Dublin, and McMurdo, though a Scot, had recently been stationed there. One might almost have thought it St. Patrick's Day by the copious flow of local gossip. He had been brought up largely by his grandfather, a hunting farmer, so there was much talk of horses, which pleased Henry.

Throughout dinner and for long afterwards, Russell—with a bottle of our best brandy conveniently positioned beside him— demonstrated his skill as *raconteur*. We could feel the menace of the hurricane of 14th November when all the army's tents on the plateau were swept away within minutes, and the long agony of the laden *Prince* and other vessels outside Balaklava harbour as they were smashed to pieces against the cliffs by giant waves.

He vividly described riding down to the plain to meet survivors of the Light Brigade as they streamed back from the massacre, and of searching frantically for friends in the various regiments and finding only a few alive, one of them Lord George Paget, whose Fourth Light Dragoons had suffered 72 casualties. Finally, of scribbling his dispatch that night to *The Times* on a saddle across his knees in a tent full of wounded and exhausted officers who, having started by prompting him, had one by one sunk into sleep.

McMurdo recounted having had his horse shot under him during a charge in the Scinde campaign. 'But I,' declared Russell with gusto, 'can claim the singular distinction of having had my house demolished around me by employees of our host of this evening!' He gave me a grin, and helped himself to more brandy: 'I, leaving my house in its usual condition, had set off on my regular three-day tour of regiments. The surrounding courtyard was in its habitual state of abomination, the favoured resort of Tartar camel drivers and drunken sailors anxious to escape the attention of the Provost-Marshal's myrmidons. When I returned I found that Beatty's navvies had pulled down the outer wall and laid a track right across my courtyard. Just as

I was entering a room on the first floor, the same men contrived to bring down a poplar neatly right across the house itself, bringing down roof, pantiles and part of the balcony, and smashing two of the remaining windows.'

What could I say? 'I bear you no malice, Jim,' added Russell. 'I put the whole incident down to sheer navvy exuberance.' We drank a final toast to 'Absent Friends' with feeling.

Smoking a last cigar before sleeping, I found myself reflecting—really for the first time—on our expedition's progress: so far, all targets had been attained—despite obstacles and without any serious delays through death or sickness. I was feeling pretty chipper about events; Henry kept bounding about in his usual enthusiastic manner; Donald was a veritable rock of reliability. I owed more to him than words could express. He was a true friend: our life together, with private jokes, helped me shrug off the weight of responsibility. I could share all my family news: he knew all about the 'imminent arrival'. 'It w-will be a boy,' he pronounced. 'You and Sarah sh-should christen him Henry James: have you thought about suitable godfathers?'

On that domestic note I enjoyed my best sleep for weeks.

* * * * * *

Good Friday dawned, raw and damp, mountain tops etched against a black sky. At that hour, both sides' guns were silent: the only sound was a bell tolling from the still-unfinished Orthodox church that mercifully had escaped the recent shellings. After a hurried breakfast, Robert put our baggage in a rear wagon and we took our places for the first run of the day up to the plateau. The four drays strained to their task, coats shining, looking like heroic horses of legend. At the Col, Swan assured me that he and his fitters would be on alert all day for the Highlanders' downward run. 'They passed here on their way up early yesterday,' he said. 'Each man was mounted on his own mule and looked highly composed—more than could be said for their dejected beasts.'

At my tent I found Kellock, cheerful though rather gaunt; he quickly had the unloading under way. I opened up my new hut to let

163

in fresh air, and settled down to write an uninterrupted report for the firm: it covered eight sheets, which ought to please them, I considered. There was no mail for me at the Post Office; nothing seemed to have gone smoothly since the old postmaster, Mr. Smith, had been moved to Constantinople. But there was some activity at the hut next to mine which was to house the electric telegraph. Two engineers from RS Newall, the makers of the cable, were busily installing instruments. 'How soon will it be operational?' I asked. 'Ask another,' they replied glumly. There had been delay in starting the actual laying of the cable from Varna across the Black Sea; then at one point it had parted! It had finally been recovered, and securely spliced. However, they told me that, even after the end had been got safely ashore near St. George's monastery, there had been further problems. Their cable terminal building had been commandeered as a Turkish hospital. Worse, a plough that had been specially designed to dig a shallow furrow for the unwinding cable, was unable to function in the frozen ground; a trench had, therefore, to be hacked out laboriously with pickaxes and shovels, to bring the line up to HQ and then on down to Kadikoi and Balaklava.

Rain fell early on Easter Saturday morning as Kellock and I watched the last stretch of track being laid to Second Division's dump by the Woronzoff Road. On the way back to our hut we were met by Colonel Paulet Somerset, Rifle Brigade, one of the ADCs: 'His Lordship,' he announced, 'intends to inspect the working party of the 71st before they entrain. His meeting with General Canrobert to co-ordinate the coming bombardment of Sebastopol is, however, still in progress.'

A more prolonged rainstorm drenched us. 'I trust the C-in-C will not leave his inspection too late,' I replied. 'The track will be slippery.'

'Correct timing of the bombardment is critical.'

'The same applies to my train.'

Colonel Somerset smiled: 'You know "Rags" well enough by now: he makes his own arrangements. He *will* inspect the men at the conclusion of the conference.'

On returning to HQ the working party was stuffed with hot stew washed down with beer, relieved at not having to go back down to camp on the backs of mules, and pleased with their performance over the two days. Despite having had two of their number wounded by Russian sharpshooters, they had tasted revenge, accounting for ten enemy gunners serving the Mamelon batteries by directing their fire from behind earth-filled gabions. After that, they said with satisfaction, the embrasures had been closed and the guns fell silent.

Kellock had marshalled three trains of four wagons each; it would take no time for them to be filled and sent on their way. The men were mustered for inspection: minutes passed; they were stood easy, but still no sign of Lord Raglan. Rain had begun again as I ran back to HQ. The meeting was just breaking up, I was assured. At long last the C-in-C emerged from the farmhouse, accompanied by three staff officers.

I felt uneasy: a heavy mist was now forming over the plateau. Lord Raglan's inspection was meticulous as though in apology for the delay. At length, I escorted him back to the head of the parade, to witness the departure of the first train down the slight incline to Swan's stationary engines. Two brakesmen had been positioned in each wagon. Lord Raglan looked pleased: so far, so good, I thought. As the second train was getting away and the rain grew heavier I could only just make out its safe arrival at the Col.

Kellock and I had planned to travel in the last wagon of the third train with the officers and some of the 71st. I could not imagine what kept the C-in-C so long in conversation at that point with Captain Macdonald, the commander of the working party…it took a prolonged burst of gunfire from Chapman's Battery to recall him to a realisation of the lateness of the hour and the worsening weather.

We set off smoothly enough; then I noticed our brakesmen having some difficulty in checking the speed. The wagon began to sway; soon it was travelling dangerously fast. 'Everyone lie down!' I shouted. Pushing one of the brakesmen aside I applied my whole strength to the lever. The brake tightened; I could hear the locked wheels skidding along the rails. Please God, I had checked the momentum! Then at a slight bend, the offside wheels lifted and I felt the wagon lurch over on its side. The coupling snapped with a crack and the wagon spun clean away, throwing me headlong to the ground. There was a momentary silence; then agonised screams rang out in the darkness.

I hit the limestone outcrop with an almighty smack, luckily with arms outstretched. It felt as though every bone in my body had been broken. Blood poured down my face from a cut on my forehead; I lay there, completely winded. A figure crawled up to me—it was Kellock: at least he could move! Soldiers were running from HQ, alerted by the noise of the crash and the cries of the injured. At that point I must have lost consciousness, and came to on a stretcher being carried up to my tent by two old orderlies. I could still hear the screams...

After a while Mike Read came in and quickly checked me over for possible fractures. 'You've been lucky,' he remarked as he sewed up my cut. I was ordered to bed: 'It's rest and soup for you—no brandy, mind.' He could tell me nothing about the soldiers' injuries or the first three wagons.

Robert carefully settled me down, piling blanket on blanket; I lay motionless, head throbbing and body aching as though I had been on the rack. My teeth were chattering uncontrollably: it was impossible to take more than a mouthful or two of soup. Any movement felt like a knife thrust, but my sharpest pain was a fear that the accident might well prejudice against the railway. There was nothing to do but live with that thought, a bitter one after all that had been achieved.

Kellock arrived, clothes mud-stained and torn, but now on his feet. His news was bleak: one soldier had been killed outright; another had had his right leg severed as the wagon crashed on top of him; half a dozen other unfortunate soldiers had been knocked about, with cuts to face and hands; one of our brakesmen was still concussed. All the officers had escaped unscathed.

'What about the other wagons?' Kellock did not know, but would find out on his way down to Kadikoi to alert Campbell. He made little of his own sorry condition, muttering merely that our escape had been 'a blessed miracle.'

I dozed fretfully through the night as the wind dashed sheets of rain continually against the canvas: they were the blackest hours I had ever endured. In a lucid spell early next morning I scribbled a note to Sarah.

Easter Saturday, 7th April, 1855.

My Ever Dearest Wife

We had a very unpleasant accident on the line last night. Lord Raglan wished 300 soldiers brought down by rail which we did with a vengeance. They were all put into three trains; the first two got down safe enough, but the third in which was myself, the officers and Kellock, ran off the line. One unfortunate soldier was killed; another will have his leg off and some half a dozen were knocked about a good deal. I got a tremendous shaking and every bone in my body aches—but nothing more. Kellock and the officers all escaped.

We are getting on well with the railway, and if they don't take Sebastopol shortly we will have it finished in a little time. I am glad to hear that dear little Fanny is nearly well and that Susy and the boy are so sound. Kiss the dear pets for Papa and believe me ever, your loving husband.

Donald's arrival was better than physic. The three wagons had, he reported, been halted before reaching the Col, and had gone safely down to the Highland camp. Swan and Kellock were checking the brakes on all wagons and would establish safe limits for loads and truck numbers on the incline. 'I'm concerned about Kellock,' he confided. 'He's t-taut as a bow string; I told him to see our doctors but he says he can't leave the job. To my mind, he should get completely away for a stretch—and so should you, too,' he added.

'Nonsense, I'm coming back to Balaklava tomorrow, and I'd be glad then, Donald, if you'd take over up here. There's another week's work still to be done on the tracks to the divisional camps.

McMurdo's going to need a good deal of help: he has rather a short fuse, I fear.'

'Jim, you're mad,' said Donald as he left the tent.

Colonel Somerset paid a short visit, at Lord Raglan's behest, he said, to enquire how I was. I'd just managed after an agonising sweat to sit upright; thank God, my head was clear, and I felt a fierce determination to get up and carry on with the job. 'You'll be getting forty-four wagons today,' I promised him, 'and forty-eight to-morrow.' He looked surprised but pleased. Robert's Easter Sunday morning gift was a huge mug of steaming tea laced with rum. Nectar! The legless soldier, he reported, was on the mend; the injured men were sporting their bandages and eating enough for a battalion. Our brakesman had recovered from his concussion; shells from the first trainload of the day were already being unloaded.

Mike Read was visibly relieved at my plea to go down next day. He gave a wry glance at the water-logged floor and the single candle with its flame blown level by the wind gusting across the bed. 'I agree, this is hardly a suitable command post,' he said, 'though you could transfer to the HQ medical centre.' I reminded him of his opinion of army medical standards: 'There's nothing like one's own bed,' I said. 'All right, we'll get you down first thing,' he said briskly. 'I'll have a covering fixed up and see you down myself.'

'Thanks!'

'But right now,' continued Mike, 'you must rest and relax—no movement, no excitement.'

'Help me fix up a low table: I've an urgent report to write for the firm first.' That took most of the afternoon, with fingers numbing, then feet; despite the blankets I couldn't stop shivering. Re-reading the report I reflected that the outcome of the accident could have been infinitely grimmer. I pulled my woollen navvy cap down over my ears and urged myself firmly to be philosophical. The hours passed, interspersed with dreams of the intransigent Commissary-General Filder—of all people! I truly was between a rock and a hard place.

16

BOMBARDMENTS

9th April

I was jerked awake at 4 am with thumping concussions coming from Chapman's Battery. Immediately the noise was amplified to a terrifying roar as guns all along our front opened up simultaneously. I sat on the edge of my bed as the tent shook with the blast, the whistle of shells merging with the deep bellow of mortars. Every weapon was being fired continuously; those nearest to me at the rate of 70-80 to the minute, I calculated: the racket was deafening—bemusing.

I slipped on my wet boots and peered out through the tent flap. A thick black fog was being driven towards our lines by the wind; the pall of smoke from the guns grew denser by the second; rain studded the deepening pools of muddy water lying right across the camp. I could see small groups of soldiers struggling to re-pitch tents that had been blown flat. In the murky atmosphere it was impossible to see any effects of our fire, and no enemy gun-flashes were visible. The Russians had been completely taken by surprise.

Mike Read was my first visitor. He had been watching the bombardment from Cathcart's Hill.

'Very few officers are out there,' he said. 'Old Sir John Campbell and an ADC spotting for Lord Raglan. I caught a glimpse of the new chief engineer, General Jones, but then he went scurrying off like a jack rabbit to visit all the batteries.' The wind was, he reported, veering a trifle to the west which would clear the smoke from our gunners' faces. His comments sounded reassuringly casual—Read, the cool veteran under fire! He started to give me a final check-over, but I stopped him. 'I'll be all right,' I said. 'What's important is for you to tell Colonel Somerset at once that Campbell will be up later today to take over from me here.' He went off quickly.

Unloading of shells from the first train of the day was badly hampered by the rain, and it wasn't until 9 am that we finally got away. Mike and I climbed into one of the wagons for the downward run; Robert threw a tarpaulin over us. Out in the open the din of the guns made speech impossible. As we approached the curve where the derailment had occurred I felt myself stiffen with apprehension, but the wagon rolled on smoothly. I took a pull at Mike's flask and enjoyed the glow in my stomach as we went down the incline. The brakes worked perfectly! At Balaklava the noise of the guns was just as loud as it had been on the plateau.

The news, which Donald poured out in a rush, was—as usual—mixed. 'Swan says the braking s-system can certainly be strengthened; his fitters are carrying out the modifications.' Donald said both he and Swan reckoned our plan to free-wheel empty wagons with brakesmen down the incline to Kadikoi was a risk well worth taking for the extra loading-time gained. 'As for the line itself, that's basically s-sound: it'll be a good all-weather track once we've consolidated some sections during the summer.' So far, so good.

The bad news was about Kellock. 'He's down with fever,' said Donald. 'It hit him suddenly after he'd been working through the night for hours on the braking tests: he w-wouldn't stop for a meal; did all the calculations crouched under the lee of a wagon to escape the rain. He collapsed as he was trying to put dry clothes on.'

'Is he in the sick bay?'

'No. Dr. Cadell said the air is pestilential here, so he got him and two other staff with fever to a hospital ship, *Cyclops*, that was leaving for Scutari in an hour. He went, too, to see them safely there. He thinks the sea voyage may do them good, and the weather will be better over there.'

'I hope it's the right decision,' I said. 'You'll not get me to Scutari—ever.'

'The s-sooner you move into that "marine residence" of yours the better I'll be pleased, Jim. You'll be up in the hills away from this reek, with a sea view and farmyard attached. Henry says he's searching everywhere for a cow.'

'I'm staying *here*—and keeping a eye on McMurdo.'

'Well, if you think you should: he'll need all the support you can

170

give him. His men have lost eighty commissariat mules—they say they just broke loose! Well, I'll get up to HQ.'

'Please God this bombardment heralds a real breakthrough,' I said urgently. I had a sudden fear that events were once again in danger of slipping away from the Allies. An army failure now would be poor recompense for all our feverish efforts to bring the railway 'into being' in time.

I was conscious of Donald's grave regard. 'Look after yourself, old friend, look after *yourself* up there.' His embarrassed nod somehow embraced us both: I felt obscurely comforted, and determined to keep any doubts I might have about long-term consequences of my 'tumble' to myself.

McMurdo was generally setting about things in an orderly enough manner, but he had a Scots temper which, I feared, Filder's tactics would all too soon unleash. Also his new habit of deluging everyone in authority with innumerable memos was causing friction—and not achieving results either. However, Willie's heart was in the right place, and his thinking was certainly on the grand scale. Russell told me after our dinner that McMurdo's first demand on Filder after disembarking was for 12,000 mules! Now he had lost 80 on his first excursion. It was important to get his Land Transport Corps up and running quickly to take over the railway as soon as possible. Every letter I was getting from the firm harped on the coming expiry of the navvies' six-month contracts and of their intention to pull back our ships. This troubled me: we needed all the men we had, to keep up with demands from the army.

Mrs. Williamson insisted I got into bed, and dosed me with the usual pills and soup, which provided some sort of barrier against the incessant drumming of the rain on our roof and the everlasting thump of the guns.

I pulled myself together later and wrote to Sarah:

Balaklava
Monday, 9th April 1855

*I mentioned in my last letter that we had had an
accident on the line; ...but I am nicely all right
again. It was an unfortunate occurrence. We have
not commenced to throw off our winter clothing
yet—I believe this is not generally done till the
beginning of May when I hope Sebastopol will be
taken. The army is very eager to go in, and once they
attack it in earnest I have little fear of the result,
although the loss of life will be, I dare say, great.*

*I shall look out most anxiously after this month
for news from and of yourself. I trust in God, my
dearest Sal, that everything will go on all right.*

*The firm have not allowed me the £250 extra
insurance; it is very shabby and they have not
treated me well. However, I have told Camidge to
make another application for it; he is as great a fool
as ever, quarrels with everyone but toadies to me
before my face...*

What with the constant irritations and daily frustrations from
Filder and his staff and the incompetence and low quality of the LTC
men, McMurdo was being driven to distraction—and so was I! HQ
was demanding an ever-greater volume of supplies by rail—very
flattering, in one way, but requiring the very deuce in time-tabling and
co-ordination to achieve. Added to that, the firm were by now
adamant about a complete withdrawal of our navvy force at the end of
their six-months' contracts. London had somehow entirely
overlooked—or ignored—the fact that it was I who had over-riding
discretion on their termination or extension, depending on our
operational position. The matter had to be cleared up immediately:
there was not a moment to lose.

I decided to set down on paper a picture of our overall
commitments and the precise deployment of our men in a factual form

that I considered would appeal to Edward Ladd Betts, even in his most nit-picking mood. I co-opted Bob Shaw for the task, and also called in Mr. Bailey, a Commissariat officer, as an independent valuer.

The stores' tables we arrived at excluded all supplies for Highland Brigade and cavalry, which had long been making full use of the line. Nevertheless, the current total of provisions alone reaching HQ came to 112 tons *daily*. A breakdown showed:

Biscuit 300 bags, 112 lb each		33,600 lb
Salt meat 100 casks 450 lb each		45,000
Groceries and extras say		30,000
Corn say 500 bags 150 lb each		75,000
Hay 120 bales 150 lb each		18,000
Fuel-wood and charcoal say		45,000
TOTAL		246,000 (112 tons)

Though impressive, this was, as I pointed out, only part of the picture. After only six weeks in full operation, the railway had supplied forward troops with approximately 1,000 tons of shell and shot, 300 tons of small arms, 3,600 tons of commissariat stores and upwards of 1,000 tons of guns, platforms, huts and QM's stores. Demands for greater volumes of guns, shells and ammunition were reaching me almost hourly.

We had also transported all material for extending the line as well as huts for our people and fuel for the stationary engines. Until the welcome arrival the previous week of 65 more drays by *Norwich*, all this work had been accomplished by our original 35 shires and 20 mules. We had, incidentally, been the means of saving the remaining worn-out artillery horses from their ceaseless killing journeys.

Equally beneficial had been the effect of the navvies who had literally taught the army how to work: 50 soldiers would now do more than double what the same number would have accomplished two months before! Also, our men had been the means of clearing Balaklava of the wretched and filthy denizens who inhabited the place and had made it a rat-infested pest house.

The manpower needs seemed to me even more clear-cut, given the pitiful performance to date of McMurdo's raw recruits. Nearly all the navvies were needed to work the line, with a brakesman to each wagon, and drivers for the LTC mules. We had so far lost only seven men through death, but the remainder were essential to consolidate and maintain the railroad. (I had heard rumours of the arrival of Sardinian army regiments; their new camp would require an additional spur to it, no question.)

It was the moment for plain speaking: 'I do not think a single navvy should be sent home. Had I double the number of carpenters and smiths they would still not meet the requirements of the army and the expedition. A few of the miners might perhaps be spared, but they are a useful class of men and the majority can always be employed in quarrying stone to the lime kilns.'

How PB&B would react was quite another matter; I had no way of judging what political or economic pressures were weighing on them. My job was only to understand—and respond to—the immediate priorities, which were to increase by every means possible the volume of shells and stores for the army, and to redouble maintenance of our all-important rail-track and minimise the pounding it was getting from ever-growing traffic.

For the first time in any of my official reports to the firm I gave vent to feelings of frustration at the attitude of our Commissary-General. 'Mr. Filder,' I wrote, 'will still make no arrangement for the issue of biscuit, salt meat and groceries at HQ though I have volunteered time and again to take everything up by rail. Even when this was finally agreed, he coolly countermanded the order—and this despite him having at his disposal every day at least 30 of our wagons, which could easily have been filled twice over if his staff could only have been brought to put in the necessary hours of work. Filder, it is clear, cares nothing for the comfort of the army: divisions still have to continue the old, futile policy of sending men down to Balaklava for their rations—*and getting them up by rail on their own account*. None of my impassioned pleas to Lord Raglan to bring about a change have had the slightest effect.'

Stone copied out my report, with a duplicate for Donald up at

HQ: I wanted his opinion before posting it off, though I felt sure he would concur in my conclusions.

At all events I was determined to have things out with Filder, once and for all: such an intolerable position could not continue. I would sooner resign than see all our efforts brought to naught. I walked—unannounced—into his office. The Commissary-General, who was alone, rose to meet me. 'Ah, Mr. Beatty,' he said in his familiar cold tone, 'I see you have come about the order.'

'What order?' I asked.

'Colonel Steele's order to establish an issue department at HQ immediately.'

I looked at him in astonishment, my hastily-prepared accusations frozen in my throat. 'I have heard nothing about such an order,' I managed to get out. 'But I am delighted at the news: it is very much overdue.' So, my pleas to Lord Raglan had been heeded!

'Your ideas and mine about timing and procedures are never likely to coincide, Mr. Beatty, even were we to work together for years,' he remarked with a venomous look in his eyes: he truly hated everything I stood for.

I laughed, a reaction really of surprise at having at last won a victory over an intransigent functionary. 'God forbid our partnership should last that long,' I replied. 'But, for the sake of the army, I will begin sending up your stores to the plateau from tomorrow.'

I was halfway to his door when he shouted: 'You do not seem to appreciate at all the position of either myself or my staff. You are nothing but a meddler, sir.'

'And you, Mr. Filder, what are you?'

'A patriot I hope, Mr. Beatty—reviled for running my department tidily.'

'Working to rule does not win a war: that's why we've been called upon.'

I shut the door firmly behind me, and added a postscript about the latest order to my report, feeling inwardly more at peace than I had for days.

The question of the future of our ships surfaced shortly afterwards. Our marine superintendent came to my office to say he had received positive instructions from Captain Andrew to send home all the vessels forthwith: *Levant* and *von Humboldt* were, however, to remain. That was the only bit of good news and I welcomed it, for *Humboldt* promised to be very handy for our purposes.

Getting back into our old Balaklava quarters was deeply repugnant; the place was swarming with huge rats that had torn our one leather armchair to shreds and half eaten one of my discarded boots. The stench of the town was viler than ever, despite all Colonel Harding's efforts to clean up the harbour. The swamp areas at the northern end had been filled in and roughly levelled; army sappers had driven in piles to create more wharf space, but still every scrap of open ground was piled high with crates and bales, lying higgledy-piggledy where they were thrown from the lighters. Each day, it seemed another new building was springing up not only in the town but also outside.

I pinned my hopes of respite on Henry who was supervising the completion of our new marine residence. Donald was, as always, the ideal colleague to leave in charge at headquarters. I wasn't surprised that Lord Raglan and he had developed a touching mutual respect, and that Donald had soon become a welcome figure at many a mess dinner.

Everybody knew everyone in Balaklava, but I was greeted by a new figure one morning at our sheds. 'I'm Roger Fenton,' he announced cheerfully. 'Here to take photographs of the campaign for Agnew, my Manchester print dealer.' His dress was meticulous by our standards, and he was self-confidence personified. He had brought introductions from Prince Albert downwards to everyone of significance in the Crimea, and mentioned that his passage on *Hecla* had been jointly secured through the Duke of Newcastle and my own master—Sir Morton Peto. The exact purpose of his mission appeared obscure but I soon got the idea—it was an attempt by those at home to put a more optimistic gloss on the sombre picture painted in Russell's dispatches.

Fenton was desperate for help: he couldn't get his horse-drawn van (which served as a dark-room) or his boxes of equipment ashore. We arranged storage room for him, and John Parker fixed him up with a bridle and saddle and a temporary stall for his horse. He set to at once, taking a lot of pictures of the railway before moving up to the plateau. The navvies were convinced he had come out to the Crimea specifically to take *their* photographs, and plagued him unmercifully. Good-naturedly, he offered to take my portrait, but I felt too strung up and out of sorts; anyway, it required a 20-second exposure!

The violence of our bombardment finally tailed off, and the noise of the guns diminished as the wind swung round firmly to the west: all that was constant, day after day, was the procession of hospital trains to the sick wharf. Our doctors and nurses were often there, lending a hand. On several occasions I saw Mother Seacole dispensing tea and wine to the injured, and handing out her little sponge cakes, a tradition she had established when she had first arrived and was living aboard *Medora*. She made them, she told me, between decks on that grim old powder ship with eggs she had had delivered from Constantinople.

Individual charity and courage was evident everywhere but precious little overall military strategy, so far as I could see. Donald remarked on one of my visits to HQ: 'The closer one g-gets to the heart of affairs, the less anyone knows what's really going on.'

What did finally become clear was that the attack on Sebastopol had fizzled out, despite heroic hand-to-hand fighting in the advanced trenches and every effort by the gunners. It wasn't only 'Field Marshall April' and his weather that finally drew the sad curtain down; 'General Rumour' had by then also joined in. Our reduced rates of firing had to do with shortages—yes, *shortages*—of fuses for the 10-inch shells, and also of 13-inch shells, for which there was an over-abundance of fuses! Too many shells were exploding pre-maturely or in the air: some dated back to 1802; some even from the previous century.

I had little doubt it was true—only the latest in a long litany of official incompetence which began with all medical and hospital equipment being left in Varna when the army sailed from there for the Crimea. A cargo of iron beds had arrived at Scutari in *Manella*, while all the legs had gone direct to Balaklava in *Jura*. Boxes unloaded on shore from lighters often went untouched and unclaimed for weeks.

One shipload of potatoes remained so long in the hold that they rotted and had to be discharged into the sea outside the harbour. Only the other day a ship overturned while approaching Ordnance Wharf and deposited 1,000 shells on the harbour bed: at least they were recoverable by divers, provided they could distinguish them from all the hundreds of animal bones tossed overboard by butchers on the ships!

I wrote to Sarah:

Balaklava
30th April 1855

...The weather is now exceedingly dry and hot: I fear it will be dreadful in the summer. However, a good beard is the best protection for one's face. One mischievous person raised an alarm in the camp by saying that an order had come out for the army to shave. The officers were in great consternation as they had thrown away the few remaining razors they had! My summer clothing is coming in useful. I am now able to come out in fresh toggery and am tolerably clean which is quite a novelty in these diggings!

I have a slight touch of stiff neck and am following Albert Howes' advice and fasting for fear of rheumatism. Fancy, I have just had a great basin of arrowroot and sherry made from the milk of a cow! This is a luxury we have now every morning, being the possessors of a very good animal Henry invested £10 in the other day: he swears she is worth £20. I am able to supply our nurses and some of my intimate friends here with milk for their breakfast. We talked about making butter, but my new cook, Brown, though a capital fellow, is not the cleanest person in the world so I dropped the idea. He is, however, a good hand at making soups from the Commissariat salt pork.

I have no end of fowls which lay nearly a dozen of eggs every morning: altogether I am in clover as far as creature comforts go. If only I could get into the country and have a bit of grass to turn my stock out on I should be all right...

17

QUESTION TIME IN HERACLEA

May

Another month, another world. The previous week had been fine but bitingly cold: one only took boots off to go to bed, with all the blankets piled high. Then followed 36 hours of continuous rain and wind: miraculously this nearly dissipated my rheumatism. The doctor took me off physic, and I indulged in a piece of mutton. By contrast, this week we had constant sunshine which brought everything and everyone to life. Dwarf roses appeared suddenly in bud and, in sheltered spots, thick drifts of mignonette, larkspur and forget-me-not.

One hardy survivor, whom I saw most mornings emerging in riding habit from *Star of the East* where she was quartered, was Mrs. Duberley—a formidable woman, wife of the paymaster of Eighth Hussars. She invariably rode a thoroughbred pony and was attended by either an aristocratic naval or army officer. Her unusual appearance and antics rather tickled the troops who christened her 'Jubilee'. One of the French regimental bands had, I was told, written a polka specially dedicated to her. All this for a woman who had also been an eye-witness of the Light Brigade's catastrophic charge! The other day she told me—with a tear in her eye—the story of how 'dear Jemmy', a little fox terrier, the favourite of the regimental mess, ran the entire length of the infamous valley with the Eighth Hussars right up to the enemy guns—and then limped back, wounded, with the survivors. He was patched up and packed off back to England to receive, said she, a deserved hero's welcome.

Today I was caught up in an even more unusual scene—low-key, to be sure, but wholly in character and, I would judge, justly historic. I was walking from my office to join two of our nurses and Albert Howes at the Sick Wharf where they were helping to unload the first

180

hospital train of the day; quietly assisting was Mrs. Seacole, who was readily distinguishable by her bright blue dress and bonnet. A small party had preceded me, coming on foot from Balaklava Hospital—in front, a slight figure in nurse's dress and scarf, a young lad at her side, and, closely following, a civilian gentleman.

Miss Florence Nightingale! There could be no doubting it.

I had heard of an intended visit of inspection by her but hardly expected to find myself actually standing beside this quiet lady who was observing the painful unloading with minutest scrutiny. As our surgeon explained the daily routine, I could see how flustered he was but she continued to listen without interruption. In due course I was introduced, and her attention was suddenly bent towards me.

'We have only just arrived, Mr. Beatty, and I am very glad to meet you so soon. News of your remarkable hospital train had already reached me at Scutari, and I was anxious to witness it in action at the earliest moment.' Miss Nightingale, I discovered, had a firm hand-shake, entirely in keeping with the impression she gave of a personality completely in control of events. She was slighter than I had pictured; she was—I knew—almost exactly my own age.

'The patients seem so comfortable,' she continued: 'They are certainly in a much easier condition than I usually observe. Tell me, how long does their journey take?'

'From railhead to this wharf, well under an hour—sometimes even a shorter time,' I replied. 'But I aim to ensure as smooth a journey as possible: the circumstances of each sick man vary considerably. One advantage of my wagons is that some kind of covering can be rigged up—sufficient anyway to keep off sun or provide shelter from rain, as necessary. It all helps, I think.'

Miss Nightingale nodded. 'You are quite right, Mr. Beatty,' she said quietly. 'Far too little weight is given to such points, yet compassion for the individual patient is a main ingredient in any healing process.'

Her voice was low, and her face pale and gentle but resolute. As she listened, she rested it lightly in the palm of one hand with the other supporting the elbow, a position that gave her countenance an exceptionally keen expression. I was captivated. She was a ready listener, and I found myself speaking of my father's hard years at his Enniskillen cholera hospital, and of our own subsequent medical arrangements for my men of the expedition.

Presently she remarked, smiling: 'Dr. Howes has already mentioned your centre and his portable surgery. I hope to see them both, but first I am invited by Lord Raglan to his head-quarters.' She introduced Mr. Bracebridge—'My faithful friend. He will tell you of my immediate programme; for the present, good-bye, Mr. Beatty.' Off she went, but her young companion lingered a moment, fascinated by our great drays. He asked their names: he could not have been more than twelve years old.

'What's your name?' I asked.

'Thomas, sir,' he replied.

'And what is a lad like you doing here?'

He drew himself to his full height. 'I'm Miss Nightingale's man,' he said in a voice of boyish enthusiasm. 'I was a drummer, sir, but I've forsaken my instruments to devote my civil and military career to Miss Nightingale.' He excused himself politely, and went off at a run after his lady, every inch a regular *enfant de troupe*!

It was hard to re-adjust to normal routines after such an encounter but the everlasting daily tour of inspection had to go on.

For myself, I could see little end to the war. Though everyone was heartily sick of the siege, and the English would gladly have stormed the place if the French had gone with them, it seemed our gallant Allies were shy! My work was nearly finished, and I didn't care how soon I went home, but I was resigned to staying and managing the line for as long as was required. My going away would upset Henry and all those others dependent on me. I couldn't have asked for more willing colleagues—and anyway I had signed for a full year.

But the atmosphere in the cashiers' department sorely tested my philosophical resolve. Meetings with Camidge had become more unnerving and surely more unpredictable of late. Unhappy fool: he was certainly mad! In our quarters one evening he had had a regular set-to with Donald, of all people. One of the doctors and I were obliged to separate them. Judging from the way he handled my own personal financial affairs, it wouldn't be long before he got into almighty trouble with the official accounts.

That morning he wasn't in the office, but there was general uproar among the clerks who had point-blank refused to work with him a day longer and were now threatening to send in their resignations. I took James Lewis, the senior clerk, a level-headed fellow, thank goodness, on one side, and promised action. I left him to pacify the others.

I walked straight across to Camidge's hut. He was lying, dishevelled, in bed, and looked sullenly at me over the bedclothes.

'What's the matter with you, man?' I asked.

'I don't feel well; haven't felt myself ever since I arrived.'

'Then, why haven't you seen one of the doctors, or Mrs. Williamson?'

'They can't help. It's this whole place, the atmosphere—you must know, Mr. Beatty. I can't come to terms with any of it.'

'Or with any of us, it seemed' I said. 'As for your accounts...'

'No reproaches, I beg you! I tell you sincerely: everything has got on top of me.'

'Your behaviour with everyone makes that crystal clear. God knows what those books of yours will reveal.'

'I need help, Mr. Beatty.'

'We've all tried our best to help you; but you've rejected every attempt.'

He was silent, fingers plucking at an unshaven chin.

'Well, Camidge,' I said. 'I am prepared to help you for the last time: I'm sending you home immediately. Get your things together: I'll tell Captain Raymond to fix you a berth. You're not to go *near* the office, mind. I shall appoint Lewis in your place, and I'm writing to Mr. Betts explaining the position.'

Camidge gave a short cry, and stuffed a blanket into his mouth.

'I never dreamed I would ever have to send a member of my own staff home in disgrace.'

'Not disgrace, Mr. Beatty,' he protested

'Disgrace is what it is—if not worse. Good-bye.'

Later that day I told Lewis of my decisions, and posted a long confidential letter to Edward Ladd Betts.

Shortly afterwards came news that Miss Nightingale had contracted Crimean fever—though 'determined to carry on as soon as she could', so ran the message. And she did just that! Only two weeks later I saw her in brilliant sunshine as she left Balaklava on her visit to Lord Raglan, mounted on a pretty mare that by its gambols and cavorting seemed sensible of the precious charge it bore. Her modest cavalcade drew an astonishing response from the rough crowd that swarmed to see her departure. Soldiers and sailors united to give her 'three times three'. Nothing like it had ever been seen before—nor since, I dared say. Typically, Miss Nightingale did return, unheralded. She re-boarded *Robert Lowe* and returned to Scutari to take command of her personal battle where every day a fresh victory had to be fought and won. I grieved that fate had prevented me from meeting that inspirational lady for the promised second time.

My worn and well-thumbed old diary of 25th May told the all-important news of my sweet Sarah and our family:

MRS. BEATTY HAS BEEN SAFELY DELIVERED OF A SON. BOTH ARE DOING WELL.

Lord Raglan sent that message down five miles after dark, with his congratulations. Weather awfully hot; almost impossible to do any work in the middle of the day. Perspiration pours down one. I'm getting as thin as a rake.

25th May

My ever dearest Sal. I was very glad to get, through Lord Raglan, the telegraphic message that we now have a son and that both you and he are doing well! You cannot think how uneasy I have been for some time as I have not had a single letter from you for three mails. I blame it all on the Post Office which has been in chaos ever since Mr. Smith went to Constantinople and we got Mr. Angell. I shall look forward to a long jaw from Eliza telling me all about 'the new young cub' as Henry styles our No. 2. They are certainly coming pretty fast though; nevertheless, for what we have received the Lord make us truly thankful, of course! You must be very careful of yourself, my dearest Sal; leave nursing the children to Maria and Eliza. I do not know how long Eliza will remain—I sincerely trust for a long time yet.

We kept the Queen's birthday yesterday, and I also drank your and the young shaver's health. Having the telegraph is a great comfort; I shall assume that you are, DV, going on all right unless I hear to the contrary.

I am enjoying my new residence amazingly—it is almost good enough for you, and the children would enjoy it as there are so many pretty views around. But the insects are dreadful: centipedes no end, ants, bugs, beetles, snakes etc., etc., not to mention flies, though they are a normal fact of life everywhere like the thousands of thieves that still swarm through Balaklava defying all efforts of the Provost's men. Cholera is again showing itself here but our camp is tolerably healthy. We have only lost seven men— with a couple of near cases today: it's generally drunken fellows that get attacked. Henry is well. The heat is terrific and makes me awfully lazy and weak;

185

*I very seldom venture very far except on the back of
my pony.*

Fuel of all kinds still in short supply, particularly coal which was
needed by the navy—also for our engines and other machinery. To
my surprise I got an urgent request from HQ to go at once to
Heraclea, on the north Turkish coast. The purpose: to make a survey
for a tramway at the coal mines there, with a view to augmenting
Allied supplies.

The trip would make a welcome change. I decided to take
Donald and a party of nine men, as well as John Wright, who had
been suffering a good deal from fever and diarrhoea and would
benefit from a sea trip. Henry was to stay at HQ and Kellock down at
Balaklava where, to my great relief, he had suddenly turned up one
morning, safely back from his stay in Scutari which I had imagined
might have been his last port of call. But there he was. Though mighty
thin, he had some colour in his cheeks. He praised the efforts of Dr.
Read who had nursed them across the Black Sea in appalling
conditions, but said that the other two staff members with him had
died shortly after arrival. I promised him an early boat back to
England, and left him busily organising a party to celebrate with
Swan, Middleton and a few others. He was going to get Fenton to
photograph the occasion—a regular fancy-dress affair.

He was more fortunate than Parson Gyngell who went down in
an acute state only a few weeks after we had had to put his colleague,
poor Thomas Fayres, on a homeward-bound boat. Before we left on
our unexpected journey I offered Gyngell the use of my marine
residence, and arranged for one of the nurses to look after him: he
looked pathetically grateful, but I fancied I would not see him again.

We left Balaklava harbour in some style in our own ship, *Baron
von Humboldt*, determined to ignore the huge waves that made her
roll from the very start. There was ample compensation, though, in the
bliss of feeling a fresh sea breeze on our faces after the stifling heat on
shore. The antics of the empty vessel effectively took our minds off
the dirty cooking, and vice versa. We had brought tents, intending to
camp out on arrival but in the end we stayed on board—less

adventurous but at least safe from fever and local infections.

We were met at Heraclea by a Mr. Barklay, one of the English engineers who had been appointed with the blessing of the Turkish Government to supervise part of the local coal mines on behalf of the British and French navies. He showed us round some of the workings which, until his arrival, were operated in very primitive fashion— hewn coal was brought to the surface in baskets by labourers and thence removed to the coast on mules.

What I was required to survey turned out to be not just a local tramway section but a long stretch near Sengalaka, an area some eighteen miles distant, through thickly-wooded country with no roads. That was a proposition needing very careful consideration.

Despite problems, our days developed almost a holiday atmo- sphere; the air was sparkling and the sun shone strongly on a myriad of scented wild flowers that grew nearly waist-high. Barklay supplied us with daily milk and fresh eggs; he even lent me books. I got my hands on a novel, *The Heir of Redcliffe*, which I found a rattling good read.

We all revelled in sea bathes, every day.

On the last evening of our visit Donald joined me on deck for a cigar; companionably we watched a spectacular summer sunset slowly fade. The sea was as still as the warm air round us. 'Perfect,' I remarked, but my thoughts were gloomy. Sarah would have been an ideal confidante at this moment, but she was busy now with her new concerns: I could not inflict problems on her by letter.

I looked across at my colleague, 'Who do you talk to, Donald, when you're feeling down—except your beard?'

'My m-mother, if at all,' he replied. 'But, bless her, there's no guarantee she'll even read my letters; leastwise, she never makes any comments on my news or answers questions.'

'Frankly, I wish profoundly I could make our firm out. On the one hand they press me for details on even the most trivial aspects of the work; on the other, they're starting a clamour for an end to all our activities here. I feel like a bone pulled in opposite directions by two fighting dogs.'

Donald gave his great laugh—a reassuring sound. 'Remember

our d-days in Canada, Jim,' he said. 'The b-best moments were always when we were away on our own with the men, and had nothing but a winter forest to contend with. Once back at base, head office letters kept pouring in—queries, orders, rarely any solutions though. And, more often than n-not, their letters out of sequence.'

It was my turn to smile. 'I'm worried by all the rumpus over my last report. Whatever possessed you to show Russell that copy I sent you, Donald?'

'He said he was short of news, and asked if I had any up-to-date information he could use. He's a friend; I didn't see any harm.' Donald clearly felt no contrition about his action.

'Well, my views as well as my figures were splashed all over *The Times*. I haven't lived it down since—especially with Filder.'

'In fairness, all Russell quoted was facts,' protested Donald. 'What really did the damage was our firm allowing the *Illustrated London News* to publish the full report, including that private postscript of yours.'

'Why do you think they did that?'

'Perhaps Mr. B-Betts believed it would strengthen your hand against red tape.'

I sighed. 'It doesn't make sense. Here's the army asking me to survey this tramway: presumably they're anxious for us to build it. Does the War Office know that our firm are planning to withdraw the navvies? Who do they think I will use for labour—McMurdo's rabble?'

'What do *you* think should be done, Jim?'

'Not build the tramway,' I replied promptly. 'But not out of pique, Donald. I shall remind the firm our men have only signed on to work in the Crimea—and nowhere else. I personally wouldn't blame them jibbing at this extra task. So fresh navvies would have to be sent out from England. That's unthinkable.'

'Agreed.'

'Besides, our men still have a full-time job running the railway, and they've all dwindled down to children in strength. '

'It may have to come down to McMurdo's men.'

'We'll get no sustained assistance there; half of them are on the sick list, and the rest thwart all attempts to teach them even the most elementary skills. They're only fit for simple work on the roads. Even at that, their methods are slovenly: I wouldn't trust any of them in charge of our drays for half an hour.'

A breeze sprang up, ruffling the water. 'Shall we turn in?' I stood up. 'Goodnight, old friend, you've been—as always—a patient listener.' I put out my hand automatically: it was met by a firm grip. My mind flashed back to that time in Mr. Peto's boardroom when Edward Betts and I had clasped hands at the beginning of the whole enterprise.

Perhaps a way out of our present impasse could yet be found. Perhaps...

18

DISARRAY AND DISPERSALS

July

For once the Black Sea belied its name: our north-east passage back to Balaklava was smooth the whole way, with the blue water mirroring a blue sky and *Humboldt*'s wake fanning out behind us wide and white. Several times, a couple of dolphins frolicked across our bows. A happy omen?

We arrived back to a Balaklava distracted and gloomy. The latest Allied attack on Sebastopol had been villainously managed: its failure had killed Lord Raglan. He had been stricken with dysentery and had died within 24 hours. His death had followed closely on that of an old comrade, General Estcourt, the adjutant-general, and his body was already on its way back to England in *Caradoc*. With it had gone, in a bunch, his ADCs, mostly family members: Lord Burghersh (Lady Westmoreland's son), Colonel Paulet (son of Raglan's brother Charles), Somerset Calthorpe (son of his niece), Nigel Kingscote (son of his sister Arabella) and Leicester Curzon (son of Lord Cardigan's sister).

I heard a report that the late C-in-C, depressed by the dismal ending of the British attack, had told his staff: 'I shall never return home: I should be stoned in the streets.' Poor bedevilled 'Rags', whatever may have been his shortcomings as a military leader, he had proved a true friend to me.

I found headquarters in complete disarray, and was sent hurriedly through to General Sir James Simpson, the new C-in-C. I had known him as chief of staff—his previous post—appointed by the Secretary for War to check on the efficiency of Raglan's entourage. He was a colourless conformist of sixty-three, and appeared quite unable to come to terms with his daunting new position, and like Raglan sadly addicted to writing reports, just like any clerk. He told me that Lord

Panmure had instructed him to take over the railway formally from 14th July! Our men's contracts would be terminated forthwith, but he begged me to stay on as chief engineer under the terms of my contract with PB&B and continue as head of the Land Transport Corps. I placed my services at his disposal: there was little else I could do.

General Simpson additionally offered me command of the new Army Works Corps that was being formed in England, but this last offer I declined delicately: nothing but a very large salary would have induced me to take it! I feared that it would fail. The post of superintendent was now to be offered to a young man, William Doyne, an Irishman; I would no doubt be meeting him in due course. The calibre of his recruits was, by all accounts, about on a par with those that had been collected for McMurdo. On every side, the future looked uncertain; I longed for some of my old energy of Nova Scotia days.

There was sad news, too, in our own ranks. During our absence, Parson Gyngell had died of fever at the marine residence. Henry had been a brick, and had sat with him the whole time: he told me Gyngell had been perfectly happy to the end. He was buried last Friday: poor fellow, he left a wife and four children: it would be a difficult letter of condolence to write.

I was troubled by another matter—one which was even more my own responsibility. It concerned 'Black Jack' Kemp, the ganger I had agreed to take, with whatever misgivings, last December. While we were in Heraclea he had killed a soldier and vanished. I got a confused story from Edgar Swan, who had seen him bring his gang down cock-a-hoop from the plateau after finishing the last stage of the line. Kemp had promptly claimed the two days off-duty that I had promised him, and had at once taken his men on a randy in Vanity Fair.

The stark sequel was whispered to me by Fishy Haddock as he lay, pale and in pain, on a bed in our medical hut. 'I don't rightly know how it happened, Mr. Beatty, and that's the truth. We was all drunk—but mellow drunk, if you get me—then 'Black Jack' swore he'd have a black-haired bitch who had just picked up a soldier. He grabbed her, but the soldier hit him with a bottle. So Kemp drew his knife and stabbed him clean through the heart. I tried to stop him but he gave me a great swipe through my side—I'm lucky to be alive, Dr. Howes says. The girl scarpered; up come a provo, and Jack took to his heels. No one's seen him since, though Barber Bill thinks he fetched up at the harbour.'

'It was him all right,' Bill told me later. 'We'd been mess mates years before on a freighter when I was seafaring for a spell in the Med. He was young, a bear of a man then—but vicious to the core. I wasn't sorry to slip ship and lose him and his tricks. Well, I was at the harbour that afternoon, and I swear I saw him boarding a Greek coaster that was just leaving on the afternoon breeze. Please God we've seen the last of him—a right deserter, he was!'

A deserter—and a deadly killer. My heart sank at the thought of the hours of enquiry and paperwork that sordid incident would cost me, yet I had to take my share of blame. I had, after all, taken him on and, to give him credit, he had fulfilled his side of the bargain—bad lot though he had turned out to be. He lacked the humanity of a Tom Grace, but if he wasn't liked by most of his men, what ganger was? He had his toadies—and made them sweat, too, as he sweated; 'Black Jack' ran his rough team brutally.

Compared to army figures, my expedition's casualties had been comparatively light. True, we had lost Gyngell and two of the staff who had died in Scutari, but only a total of 46 in all—22 navvies, eight drivers, four miners, three fitters, two smiths, two horse-keepers, one clerk—and now a 'deserter', as Bill had put it. Still, that represented nearly 50 out of a total of 580 men in just eight months—a large enough figure, in all conscience. Some had merely had bad luck; one could only feel sorry for the navvy who had popped his head up out of a lime-kiln quarry to watch the firing and had it taken clean off by a cannon ball. But, DV, I would be getting the bulk of our people home before fever and the pestilential climate did for all of them. It was with a real pang that I thought of Tom Grace who had been ailing for weeks but still struggled on: a charge of home-bound sea air might just restore him. I profoundly hoped so. He had given me whole-hearted loyalty and the shrewd advice of a father; the least I could do would be to return him to his family alive. Henry, too, had to be put on an early boat if his health was to be rescued; I would sorely miss his company.

I settled down sombrely with Donald and McMurdo to review the new manpower situation as it would affect the railway: the immediate need was to establish a hard core of the most trustworthy LTC men to act as a strike force in emergencies. The list we drew up was far from impressive, but McMurdo appeared confident, and we had all been impressed by the vigour shown by his subordinate, Captain Powell. What was patently lacking—and it was a yawning gap—was the experience and ballast that could only be provided by navvies bred to the job. It was a comfort to know that Donald would be there with me during the next few anxious months: McMurdo, for all his keenness, could not be expected to work miracles single-handed.

The C-in-C and General Jones, the chief engineer, were placing far too much faith in the support an Army Works Corps might provide. That body had not yet even embarked for the Crimea, though I saw from the papers that they had been kicking up a shindy in London: they would be a troublesome lot to deal with out here.

Serious fighting had almost ceased along the front but not the sickness, aggravated by oppressive heat. We had dry scorching winds and tremendous thunderstorms when the rain fell in a silent sheet: one deluge drowned a navvy—and numbers of cattle.

For some time now we had stopped working the men in the middle of the day to conserve their strength, but all sense of purpose and urgency by the military had completely evaporated.

Many of the old army friends I made last winter had either gone home or been killed.

The staff at HQ had all changed now—I *disliked* unfamiliar faces. The new C-in-C had not won the confidence of the army; there was even talk of another general coming out. Personally, I wished they would hand over command to some intelligent ensign instead of the old fogies who had had control so far with such disastrous consequences, all severely short-sighted in every way!

Our own work was certainly not helped by the prevailing attitude of both officers and men. Sensing that pressure was off, they were diverting themselves in traditional ways—the officers with horse-racing and cricket matches; the men with football and races run against their French comrades. Navvies spent their off-duty time drinking recklessly at Vanity Fair. Though the vile stuff made them the first to fall ill, they just could not be made to comprehend that their life hung on a thread: all they thought about, if at all, was their chance of getting home—getting away almost anywhere from where they were.

Last week I had sent home 105 men in *Wildfire*: another 90 would go next Monday, and 150 the following week. The remainder might have to wait for a vessel to take them. Henry went off quite philosophically in *Albion*, along with the bulk of the staff: the strain of life here had almost worn them away. Soon I would be the sole survivor, with Donald and the faithful Stone who still copied out my long reports to the firm with meticulous accuracy. In that sense, nothing had changed!

On board 'Humboldt'

Sarah, I hope you got my letter written from Heraclea and were able to make it out: I had to write on my knees as the ship was rolling about a good deal. I long to get back to Balaklava and hear how you are: I trust in God you are all well.

I am glad that Captain Mason got my letter and agreed to stand godfather to the boy: he is one of the most honourable and high-minded fellows that I know out here—and very well off. He tells me he has resigned sea matters and is going to get married and settle down as a respectable man! I was astonished to learn that dear Lord Raglan's Christian names were James Henry! Only fancy, if you had transposed the names, our little chick would have had the same as him. He was a splendid old fellow— and the first man who announced the intelligence of Henry's birth to me. His death has for the moment

194

paralysed everyone here; the siege still drags its slow length along. I should not wonder if the army had another winter of it here.

I am so glad you are off to Brighton, as Dr. Clarke seems so positive about it. I sincerely trust Eliza will go with you: I would be exceedingly anxious if you had charge of all the chicks yourself. You cannot be expected to have recovered your strength quite yet. Do not be worried about the expenses of lodging; poor Nan-Nan's health is of far more importance than any money. Do not hesitate to make use of Steinhauser in any way he can help.

Henry and I are much more comfortable now than before. I have kept the nurse who attended old Gyngell to look after the house for a month and give her a rest—comparatively speaking—after her late fatigue. She seems a very respectable woman, and I have even been able to get a little washing done. Last night I had the extraordinary luxury of sheets for the first time this six months! But I did not care much for them: one sweats so much that they are quite damp in the morning, which is not by any means pleasant or conducive to health. I think I shall discard them again. If you and the chicks benefit from the sea air, stop August and September, or get Steinhauser to find some place for you in the country and go out of town. Do not stint yourself for want of another servant.

Men and staff are all anxious to get home; the cholera has thinned them dreadfully and caused quite a panic. I wish to goodness I was going with them: a week or two in England would make a man of me again after the voyage. Ethelbert Blake is ill again and wants to be sent home which he finds some difficulty in managing. He has become a tremendous grumbler—just like his father. Camidge is gone home in disgrace. He was a most infernal scoundrel; I have heard of more gross transactions of his since he went away.

I spent a couple of pleasant days on Lord Ward's yacht cruising down to Yalta and Alonata with no end of swells on board. Colonel Ridley told me that everyone was making their billets snug for a second winter in the Crimea! There are some pretty places along the coast. Prince Woronzoff has a delightful villa and a fine deer park that we could see distinctly from our vessel. I'm convinced there could be many worse places to live in than the Crimea if only it had a healthy climate. I hardly know what I shall do when all the fellows have gone; my housekeeper must go with the other nurses—she will be a real loss as I have had the house clean and my socks and flannel shirts washed since she came—a great luxury.

Now I cannot get a pocket handkerchief washed under 3d, and a pair of socks the same.

I have asked Stone to come and live with me as some sort of company, now that Henry has gone. Both William Ayling and his brother Robert—the latter very seedy looking—both left on Albion. I cautioned William when he determined to become a gentleman that I would not take him back again. He did not behave at all well, and Robert turned into one of the most idle good-for-nothing fellows I have ever met.

I am in the greatest bother about man servants: one cannot get any but tearaways or such like, and these vagabonds ask 9s or 10s a day wages.

I sent home by Henry: 3 large jars of spirits of wine, 1 box of soap, 1 new rifle, 2 parcels for Mrs. Ridley. See that he delivers them safely: the first two items will come in useful for the house and were of some to me here. Tell him the cat has come back. I believe she has a kitten, but she keeps it concealed from me.

Donald and I are now busy laying out a line for the French to Kamiesch and also a branch for the Sardinians off our Kadikoi line. It is a pity that all staff and men have gone home as I am hard up for assistance. I am shortly going up to HQ to meet the Duke of Newcastle who has come out at his own expense to judge the campaign for himself. He has recently been sick on board the flag-ship Royal Albert, but no one has expressed any sorrow about that!

I really cannot form an idea of what my movements are likely to be. If the Government are determined to keep me out here I must remain and endeavour to get the best of terms I can—and three months' leave of absence. It would suit me very well if I could truly keep on and get another year's salary out of them.

I trust, my dearest Sal, that you and the chicks are all well. With love to Eliza and kisses for yourself and the dear children.

PS Tell Henry from me not to give my address in London to anyone of the expedition, otherwise you will be plagued to death with men and their wives.

Donald and I spent an unexpected few hours last evening at the new British Hotel as 'dinner' guests of Mrs. Seacole, the proprietress. It's her pretty way of thanking us for assistance in helping transport materials and stores for her during the building period. The meal was a treat—her famous Welsh rarebit, roast pork and rice pudding, washed down by some very decent claret; and the good lady attended us personally. Though only just completed, the place had quickly become a rendezvous for officers, who used it as an informal club. There was a separate room for soldiers where she dispensed sausages (from her own pigs) and mashed potatoes. Beer she permitted but no wine or raki: it was the most decorous in the peninsula.

'Spring Hill', as it was widely known, was a remarkable establishment, with a huge Union Jack fluttering from the roof. It was easily the largest structure in the area, with buildings and yards covering over an acre of rising ground outside Kadikoi. Mrs. Seacole told us it had cost her £800 and was almost entirely constructed of discarded timber gleaned from the harbour. She and her cousin had supervised the work which was carried out by two sailors she had hired—'Big Chips' and 'Little Chips'—and two Turkish carpenters. She was also helped by a Turkish officer whom she called 'Ali Baba', who gave her four windows and a glass door from a village his company had captured.

His commanding officer, a Pasha, had become an *habitué*, and wheedled Mrs. Seacole into teaching him English. 'He came most days,' she told us, 'with a servant who sat at his feet inserting red-hot pieces of charcoal into his pipe at intervals. Sometimes he ordered his band down from their camp to play for us. Once I thought a tune seemed almost familiar; I discovered on enquiring that it was in fact *our* national anthem!'

That evening she was being advised in the kitchen by M. Alexis Soyer, the enthusiastic French chef from the Reform Club, in London, who was busy reorganising the army's cooking methods and whose novel camp cookers we had taken up in quantity to the divisions on the plateau. He was a flamboyant character, notable for his high consumption of champagne while demonstrating his culinary skills, and was accompanied everywhere by a deferential mulatto secretary. I admired his drive and cheerful determination, and was pleased when he approved of our standards of navvy cooking—both in quality and quantity.

Brisk business was going on all the time in the store alongside the hotel; it sold everything from an anchor to a needle. Mother Seacole had a tough way with thieves, and kept a double-barrelled pistol under her pillow at night, she told me. The place was also over-run with rats, she said, but the problem had been temporarily solved when a Coldstream officer lent her his pet cat, 'Pinkie'. Sadly, after three weeks, it returned to its master's quarters three miles away—obviously replete!

The next time I saw Mrs. Seacole was two weeks later on a battlefield bandaging wounded soldiers.

19

FALL OF THE FORTRESS

8th September

For some weeks the Russians had been showing great activity on the heights beyond the Tchernaya River and their numbers were being reinforced by new infantry corps, according to reports from deserters. There was mounting tension among the French, Turkish and Sardinian camps guarding the wide triangle of the plain on the left bank of the river. I was fully occupied marking out the new route for the Sardinians whose line extended from the Traktir Bridge—the French centre—east to the wooden bridge at Tchorgonna in exposed positions on the hills. Under General Della Marmora, they were hastily strengthening their defences. They had suffered cruelly since their arrival: some 2,000 of their original 16,000-strong force had succumbed to cholera, but they had maintained soldierly behaviour throughout and were widely admired: certainly their band music easily topped that of the French camps for style.

The Russian attack was launched by infantry units that had descended from the Mackenzie and Aitodor Hills during the night, strenuously supported by an artillery barrage. Everything was obscured by mist from the river and smoke from the guns, but the main thrust was aimed at the centre of the French position on the river. Had it succeeded the enemy would have been able to sweep right down to Balaklava and utterly destroy it. I could do nothing but listen in anguish to the rising clamour of the massed guns and the continuous crackle of musketry. It was a most anxious, drawn-out day. A truce was agreed at length, to collect the wounded and bury the dead on both sides: the attack had failed, and the Russians had received a terrible drubbing. I went over the field of battle next morning: a fearsome sight. Right across the plain between the

Fedukhine Heights and Traktir Bridge, Russian dead lay strewn in all directions, heaped one upon another, shattered by cannon rather than by musket or bayonet. As was their custom, they had charged in dense columns and had been shot down in ranks at a time.

The looks of agony on the faces of wounded were dreadful: they kept trying to raise themselves up, then falling back with a groan. I saw Mother Seacole tending one unfortunate after another, her mule beside her bearing satchels of bandages, medicines and cooling drinks. Four days after the battle I rode over the area again; the dead were still lying thick upon the ground, with burial parties active on both sides. For the sake of common humanity the French had agreed to bury all the dead—without distinction of nation—on the left bank of the Tchernaya, and the Russians those on the right. The river had become so choked with corpses and dyed with blood that orders had to be given that no cavalry horses should be watered there. The Russians lost some 7,000 men, plus 500 unwounded taken prisoner. French and Sardinian casualties were around 1,800 soldiers. From the number of bottles I saw lying around it was obvious that the Russian soldiers had been drinking heavily before the attack: some of the prisoners said the distribution of brandy had followed a reading by Prince Gortchakoff, their commander, of an exhortatory letter from the Czar to his troops. The Emperor of All the Russias could not have put much value on the lives of his subjects!

The new Army Works Corps had nearly all come out, and a most idle lot of vagabonds they were, too. I thought our men bad enough, but that lot beat them hollow! Mr. Doyne looked somewhat bemused as he contemplated his 'Corps' in cold blood, especially after I had explained to him the precise nature of the tasks which he would have to tackle.

The primary consideration was, of course, maintaining the railway at peak efficiency. We agreed that 200 of his most able men would start work immediately under my direction in ballasting, draining and consolidating the line along its whole length; they would also be laying rails and sleepers for the new branch to the Sardinian camp. I intended to run locomotives right along that whole level stretch, but that was some way in the future since I had only just managed to get orders for the required engines cleared through General Simpson and the War Office.

Doyne was energetic, with a sound railway engineering background, and possessed of an impatient desire to make his mark speedily. That attitude sometimes led to coolness between us, as he resented being advised! However, he soon became so overwhelmed with work as to leave little time for the trading of incivilities. His latest order from Sir Richard Airey, the QMG, was for nothing less than the construction of an all-weather road all the way from Balaklava to the front lines.

'I conceive the road,' said Doyne, 'as being twenty-eight feet in width, with all ancillary works in proportion—banking, bridging, drainage and so on.' That seemed to me a highly ambitious project that could well swallow up thousands of labourers and pack animals. Doyne added: 'I am also charged with responsibility for building several depots and stores for the Commissariat Department and for enlarging quays and wharves at Balaklava.' All this would have to be undertaken with the most unpromising human resources imaginable. I was impressed by his unwavering resolve, but not at all by his overbearing manner.

The desperate Russian offensive at Traktir Bridge had at last galvanised our army chiefs into serious action. All performances of farces at the 'Theatre Royal', Naval Brigade, and at 'Theatre Français', Karmeisch, were cancelled; work on the sap approaching the enemy defences at the Malakoff was intensified; new siege batteries were planted.

So near now were our advanced trenches that gabion-parapets afforded little protection from Russian balls and bullets: working parties and trench guards were swept away, and the toll of our dead and wounded swelled mercilessly day by day. A huge explosion was caused when a 13-inch shell fell into the entrenchments of the Mamelon and fired a French magazine containing 15,000 lbs of powder: the immediate area was devastated and littered with mangled bodies. Yet the Allied build-up was pushed ahead fiercely.

I was continuously up and down the line overseeing its smooth running: the railway was being worked to full capacity, with some

138 wagons in use each day. As well as increased quantities of ammunition—particularly heavier calibre shells—we were moving medical stores up by the ton. Everywhere trenches were being strengthened and batteries brought to full pitch. In anticipation of casualties, the field hospitals were being cleared out; all who could bear the journey came down the line and were dispatched to Scutari.

A decisive stage of the long siege was approaching—perhaps a last chance before autumn storms again enveloped the Chersonese. (In the event, weather during September and October proved the most benign in living memory.) Hopes were raised by rumours reaching the Allied camps that the Russians inside Sebastopol were becoming discontented—even disorderly—as the vertical storm of mortars blew away the house roofs. Reports spoke of bread and other provisions failing. We could see large convoys of stores and property passing regularly from the south side of the harbour to the north.

The Allied front extended seven miles, from the Sapoune Heights to Quarantine Bay, and the lines of trenches and parapets stretched some 70 miles. Given everyone's impatience to see a successful end to the long and bitter siege of Sebastopol, it was only human nature to gloss over the truly bizarre dispositions of the Allied forces, spread out as they were with their camps and siege works, right along the deeply-ravined plateau on the southern side of the city.

The northern side was firmly in Russian hands; nothing we might try could prevent reinforcements and supplies reaching the defenders; additionally, on the more distant heights great batteries had been sited. Neither could the harbour be attacked by our navy; its entrance was effectively blocked by a line of sunken warships, backed by fully-manned forts and a huge concentration of heavy guns.

British troops were all positioned to the south-east; their main objective, as I understood it, would be the taking of the fiercely-defended Redan. The French had command of the entire south-western front. Their initial targets were to be the formidable bastion of the Little Redan, and the 'Curtain'—a continuous line of defences armed with sixteen guns and a parallel parapet within, also armed. The final focus of the onslaught would be on the mighty stone-towered Malakoff—the key to the city.

This daunting stronghold had been feverishly enlarged and strengthened by the Russians over the months. It was protected by palisades of sharpened stakes, and earthen parapets of enormous thickness and height. Behind was a wide ditch, and then three tiers of batteries with 60 large-calibre guns, rising one above another. Lastly, there was a *place d'armes*, with powerful defensive infantry.

Everywhere troops were on the move: I could form no idea of the total numbers that would be committed in the coming battle—possibly 50,000, or more. By that stage my mind could only register small figures—the individual ones of old military friends or newer acquaintances.

All was set for the fifth bombardment of the fortress to which all our frantic efforts of the past few weeks on the railway had been concentrated. Hopefully, said HQ, this time it would lead to its capture.

Firing began at dawn on 5th September with the French simultaneously opening four miles of cannonading. With many others I watched this stupendous assault from Cathcart's Hill, feeling the ground shake with the reverberations. Clouds of earth were sent up and batteries disrupted right along the Russian front. The horizon was buried in smoke and vapour; the air was filled with vivid gleams and trains of fire. Meanwhile, English batteries were in concentrated action on the south-east, and mortars targeted ships in Sebastopol harbour.

One's every sense was buffeted: it seemed impossible that such a remorseless barrage could continue, but it did, throughout the day and the following night, denying the enemy any opportunity to repair shattered parapets and embrasures. Next morning the bombardment was renewed, with pauses only to allow guns to cool. A similar pattern was repeated on the following day and night: I would remember the continual concussion of explosions that assailed me at whatever point of our line I was then at.

Early on the morning of 8th September, I went up again to Cathcart's Hill to witness the final scene. The weather was tempestuous, matching the wild nature of the action. Heavy clouds of dust blown by the cold northerly wind obscured the view, but I could just see waves breaking at the harbour mouth and washing over the frail-looking bridge the Russians had hastily finished building. Connecting the south and north shores, it was formed of rafts moored side by side.

During the morning I could see part of the town in flames. French and English gunners were keeping up a remorseless fire, to which the Redan and Malakoff batteries replied with only a few shots. But were the defenders merely lulling our troops into a false confidence?

At 11 am General Simpson and his staff passed me on their way to the battery on our left, but the dust and smoke were blowing in that direction and it was evidently not the best place for seeing what was going on. I moved to the right to get a full view of the Malakoff Heights, and the dun-coloured parapets of the Redan on which the assaults were to be made, at noon.

Five minutes before that time French mortars opened up in the hope of catching the enemy unprepared, for they were accustomed to a mid-day rest during which their ramparts were not normally fully manned. Troops of the Light and Second Divisions, with 48-hour rations, were deployed in the front parallels for the assault. Elements of cavalry had been brought to the front and formed a chain of sentries to keep away amateur spectators, the so-called 'Travelling Gentlemen'. The Highland Brigade, which had marched up from Kamara, took position in the rear of the right attack, with a brigade of Guards near them. The Third and Fourth divisions formed the left attack and the reserve.

I observed with amazement mingled with dismay the arrival of our army chiefs to survey the operation: worn-out elderly gentlemen, muffled against the cold windy morning—the very antithesis of a martial presence. The picture epitomised for me the whole war: the total lack of vigour and up-to-date experience in the field, of our most senior officers. Those 'Peninsular heroes' had degenerated into decrepit old men, while competent 'Indian officers', debarred as they were by Queen's Regulations, had been given little chance to demonstrate their abilities in the campaign. I could understand McMurdo's feelings of frustration.

The bombardment ceased at noon exactly, and French storming parties advanced from their trenches, preceded by riflemen, sappers and miners. Using portable bridges as ladders, they crossed the ditch and scaled the parapet with amazing rapidity. It was a severe struggle up the slope to the key objective—the old stone tower of the Malakoff. Cruel hand-to-hand fighting with rifle, pistol, sword, bayonet, pickaxe, gun-rammer and stones. Then the tricolour standards were planted above the parapet. For six hours all Russian attempts to regain the Redoubt were beaten off by exultant engineers and Zouaves and reinforcements quickly sent in by General Bosquet.

The British story at the Redan was, sadly, not one of an equivalent victory: in just two hours our attack was halted by enemy troops and venomous fire. One could only watch in sickened disbelief as masses of Russian infantry hunted our men down and threw them back into their advanced trenches. Confusion was widespread; no second assault on the Redan was mounted.

But, during the night, the whole of the Russian army appeared to be retreating to the north side of the harbour! Flames began to rise right across the city; great explosions shook the air; murky smoke mingled with the leaping flames from burning buildings which lit up the whole harbour. There, Russian warships were being scuttled, disappearing one by one beneath the waves. The long hours were punctuated by the roar of huge explosions. First the Flagstaff Battery was blown up; then the Garden Battery was reduced to rubble. Fort Paul and Fort Nicholas were set on fire and devastated, along with the Central and Quarantine Bastions.

As dawn broke, long columns of infantry, sailors and inhabitants of the city were still making their perilous retreat north along the temporary floating bridge. At 7 am on 9th September, after the last battalion of infantry had passed over, the Russians defiantly broke the bridge.

Sebastopol had been finally abandoned by the enemy after a siege lasting 49 weeks. A towering pillar of black smoke marked its death. The menacing fortress had fallen at last. But the bitter cost of that triumph had still to be reckoned.

20

THE HOMEWARD RUN

25th November

I left Balaklava that afternoon in a snowstorm, a passenger aboard *Thames*, the first steamer I could get on which was making direct for England. I had been granted leave on medical grounds. Despite all dieting, fasting, pill-taking, I had been unable to rid myself of the accursed rheumatism in my head. On a recent trip to Constantinople with my friend Captain Stone in *Arabia* I had slipped across to Scutari for a consultation: but the physicians at the Barrack Hospital there had told me bluntly they could do nothing for me. Then old Dr. Simpson of 71st Regiment who was attending me, insisted that only complete removal to England would effect a cure.

Lord Panmure had just offered me an engagement as head of the railway for another year; all the military authorities and departments had put themselves out to be of assistance: General Codrington, the new C-in-C, had agreed immediately to my application for sick leave; the chief army engineer, Major-General Jones, had expressed his earnest hope for my speedy return. It was unfortunate that Colonel McMurdo would also be leaving for home at the same time. He had worked hard and long with his difficult LTC men, but when his wife had come out to Balaklava she found him in the highest stages of fever, and had, poor woman, a month's nursing before her. Willie had survived a coma and was now safe; but he would be a considerable— if only temporary—loss to the railway.

Fortunately, Donald, as my official second-in-command, was more than capable of taking control in our absence. He had been in the best of health and spirits throughout our labours, and a great comfort to me. It was fitting that his was the last face I saw from the boat deck as we left the harbour: that familiar towering figure in woollen cap, oilskins and thigh boots who had been the first to greet me on my arrival at Balaklava eleven months before. Standing alone on the railway wharf he waved again now—both arms characteristically aloft—until a curtain of snow driven by the bitter wind blotted him from sight.

How much I looked forward to our reunion in that strange terrain we had both helped to alter beyond belief! The Balaklava I was leaving was unrecognisable from its appearance a year ago. Huts and sheds now covered the whole town and stretched up the surrounding hills, with some tents still dotted in between. There were coffee houses, too, and some shops—even a library for the troops! The first of our locomotives had recently arrived from England—'Alliance' and 'Victory'—arousing immense interest and high hopes. Russell confided how strongly our 'whistling locomotives' put him in mind of the familiar sounds of Wolverhampton and Didcot: 'They make me believe for a moment,' he had declared, 'that we are in a civilised country!' Alas, those engines had proved of insufficient power for our motley assortment of wagons with their differing buffer heights.

It was some weeks before we got more powerful locomotives shipped over and were able to contemplate running regular services. Eventually, we worked the new engines from 7 am to 7 pm, hauling 120 or so wagons daily on an eighteen-minute journey across the plain. It was our railway's last flourish, and it satisfactorily rounded off the system I had striven for so long to bring about. But, proud as I was of our gleaming new monsters, it was our indomitable drays that still held first place in my heart.

Things mechanical had also taken a decided turn for the better with the arrival in October of the floating factory, *Chasseur*, which was put under my command. We were fortunate in its manager, Mr. Frazer, a Tyneside engineer, who knew exactly how to equip and operate such a novel vessel. In addition to turning lathes, planing and drilling machines, forges and a steam hammer, it possessed two sawmills, a brass furnace and a cast iron foundry. There were also four smiths who fashioned axles for the LTC. Given Frazer's zeal and ability, commissions for all kinds of work had poured in. In its way, *Chasseur* served the army as well as the floating bakery *Abundance* satisfied the troops' hunger, which, when I left, was producing 18,000 lbs of bread a day.

One villain who had caused me great anguish, 'Black Jack Kemp', had vanished completely. He had been the worst blot on our expedition's reputation.

As a final bonus, but far too late for my peace of mind, Commissary-General Filder had been retired by a Medical Board. He was seventy-four! His place was taken, with immediate beneficial effect, by Sir George Maclean, tough yet flexible, from the Turkish contingent.

I went thankfully below deck to thaw out. *Thames* was carrying only a few passengers—indeed, it was largely empty, a state that became uncomfortably apparent as we plunged through the steep, whipped waves of the Black Sea. At least, I had the luxury of a cabin to myself where I could stretch out and ease my head or reflect on our expedition.

I remembered a story concerning Donald that Roger Fenton had told me shortly before he went home ill—one that Donald would never have mentioned to me himself. 'Soon after the Sardinian regiments had taken up their positions,' said Roger, 'Donald and I and some other officers had gone swimming in the Tchernaya River. Riding home, we saw a Sardinian soldier in difficulties: then he disappeared under the water. As we started to strip off, Donald plunged in fully dressed—without even removing his glasses—and pulled the drowning man out by his hair. Later, the man came back with his companions to thank his saviour. With no language in common, he tried to show his gratitude by pulling out his purse and offering it to Donald. By then, I may say,' said Roger, laughing, 'Donald had stripped completely naked and was vainly trying to wring out his clothes. He'd even taken off his boots!'

I was glad to have finally finished the Sardinian branch of the line, and happy that the railway was in generally good shape for the coming winter. I had sometimes, in my innocence, toyed with the idea of one day making a cruise at leisure through the Mediterranean and taking a look at Greece and Italy. But now that was all bosh—or 'Yuk' as the Turks said all the time. *Home*, as fast as possible, was my sole cry! I found I was watching our slow passage through the

Bosphorus and the Sea of Marmara and out into the Aegean with as little interest as I would contemplate a day-trip down to Tilbury in a Thames barge.

Without warning, I began to experience a succession of troublesome dreams: it was as if, against my will, I was being forced to re-live—in detail—those last days of the fall of Sebastopol when so many of my friends had lost their lives. That last assault in September had undoubtedly been the hardest job of the war, and had matters been better managed then and afterwards by our military chiefs, the turn of the year might well have seen the enemy driven from the Crimea. As it was, orders had been given for troops to hut themselves for the winter; nothing would move until next spring, and a strong Russian presence was still in evidence on the northern side of the city and on the heights above Mackenzie's Farm.

There was no question, the enemy had held out valiantly against the Allied onslaught; never again could their fighting qualities be taken lightly. During the last decisive struggle, the French too, had acquitted themselves admirably; without their tenacity and bravery the place would never have been stormed. Sadly, as it turned out, the British plans for attack proved woefully inadequate, and our men did not perform well—there was a strong suspicion of cowardice among one or two regiments.

It was understandable, if regrettable: men who had for months been fighting behind batteries and gabions could not be brought to march steadily under fire from which they could get no cover. Referring to that assault on the Redan, the new chief of staff, Colonel Windham, whose courage and leadership during the battle had been outstanding, was heard to remark: 'The men, the moment they saw a gabion, ran to it as they would to their wives, and would not leave its shelter.'

But the 97th (Earl of Ulster's) behaved like heroes, and lost officers and men accordingly. Two good friends of mine, Colonel Handcock, who led 200 stormers, and Major Welsford, were killed outright, and poor Woods had a narrow escape—two of his fingers were shot away. The 90th (Perthshire Volunteers) lost seventeen officers killed and wounded, and the 30th a similar number. Unlucky

Captain Hammond of the Rifle Brigade, only three days out from England, was struck down early on. In 62nd Regiment, 180 men went into the attack, and 105 were killed or wounded; the 55th, 400 strong, lost 140. So the melancholy list could go on.

But my dreams were not so much about individual comrades as about the shattered remains of buildings and those shattered with them that I saw on all sides when I first rode round Sebastopol, two days after the surrender. I was disgusted to come across two sight-seeing English women calmly riding round with an escort of officers: that ladies could bear to witness such scenes of horror passed my comprehension.

Explosions were going off continually, for the Russians had mined the town as well as setting it on fire. All streets were places of peril—five French officers had already been blown up—but that did not deter scavenging French and English soldiers. Having discovered Russian cellars, many lay dead drunk in the gutters while others danced unsteadily around, dressed in Russian women's dresses and bonnets. Many more were systematically looting the houses. I saw one Zouave, with a Russian helmet on his head, carefully driving a pig before him; in his arms he carried a dead sheep, a cloak and a samovar.

Whole areas of the city had been literally ploughed by our 13-inch guns, and shell fragments and round shot lay everywhere. By the Little Redan, where scores of Russians had fallen, the ground was covered with patches and half-dried pools of blood, caps soaked in blood and brains, bayonets and broken guns. The Redan itself, for all its skilfully-constructed defences, its bomb-proof niches and little huts where officers and men had lived while on duty, had been reduced to ruins; all that remained were a few pictures, books, cards and some china from dinner services. Earlier that day 700 of our men had been buried in a trench at the foot of the steep parapet by the Anglican chaplain to the army, Reverend Parker.

Having only observed the Malakoff before from a distance, I was astounded to see at close quarters the strength of its construction and the intricacy of its internal works. It had been so designed that unless a shot fell precisely on the right spot it could do no harm. Concealed underground were officers' and men's huts and a mess-room, complete with glass lamps and packs of cards. The Malakoff was the undoubted masterpiece of General Todleben, the architect of Sebastopol's defences, and might justly have been considered impregnable. In its magnitude and solidity it was—in its way—a structure worthy of a Brassey or a Peto! In the end it had fallen only to a French surprise attack at mid-day, during a brief Russian rest period.

From Cathcart's Hill Sebastopol had always appeared white, almost untouched. Now I was seeing a totally different picture: walls reduced to rubble, roofs riddled, the green cupola of the cathedral split and splintered to ribands. Parts of the town were almost unendurable from the heat of burning houses. The quarter allocated to the French was large but, apart from the Court of Justice building and two churches, it consisted mainly of street after street of ruined dwellings in which greyhounds and mastiffs wandered, bewildered.

The English quarter, with Colonel Windham as its commandant, was on the south side. The docks themselves were in good condition, capable of taking six line-of-battle ships, with room for three more in a basin. All the walls were of white stone, capped with red and grey granite: the great gates were English-made! In one dock, a half-finished steamer was burning.

The customs house was largely undamaged, but as I approached the hospital building I became aware of an abominable stench. The dreams I was presently having—nightmares, more like—were all about that place. As if in warning, all were invariably preceded by that sickening odour from the hospital precincts.

Between 600 and 700 bodies had been discovered there the day before my visit. Some were on beds, some on ward floors, some on the hospital steps and on the stones outside—many in various stages of decomposition. Medical officers, with orderlies in attendance, were beginning an initial examination as I arrived. It took four days to bury those dead. In their retreat, the Russians had simply abandoned their men with unbelievable callousness. The dying and the deceased had been heaped together, one upon another, some still on rough pallets. The vaults below were packed with bodies: many had been there for days. There were swollen corpses, teeth tightly clamped on blackened, protruding tongues: the smell of putrefaction was overpowering. In one vault, orderlies had uncovered, under a final layer of corpses, one man still alive, half-crazed by the pain of his wounds and by thirst. He was naked and yelling; he had been there three days. He was an English officer of 90th Regiment. Outside the hospital, huge pits had been dug into which the Russians had thrown their dead like pigs— 100 to each pit.

Not even brandy nor pills could erase that diabolical scene from my mind, nor soften the anguish of those vivid dreams. I spent hours on deck, breathing in the salt air—deeply, deeply; but the wind was relentless and as cold as a knife. I took myself and my troubled mind back down to my cabin again, no fit company for anyone, least of all our captain with his continual banter. I had got used to my head throbbing, but the pain was beginning to spread down to my face and jaw. It made a man downright peevish!

I felt a new sympathy for Henry Stone, realising what he must have silently endured at my hands during our time together at the marine residence. I was forever ordering him to make tea or arrowroot—and then refusing to drink it: bullying him tremend-ously to let me have an occasional cigar, though the doctor had strictly forbidden smoking. My excuse?—the pain sometimes drove me wild. There was precious little evidence of the 'angelic disposition' which—Sarah once told me—had quite won her heart when we first met!

Mercifully, those dreadful dreams became less frequent, and my last memory of Sebastapol was of Mrs. Seacole, colourful as ever, in yellow dress and bonnet, bandaging a row of wounded soldiers outside the hospital while her mule stood patiently beside her. She had held up something in her hand: 'Look, Mr. Beatty, at my loot,' she called with a wide grin. It was a decorated altar candle she had picked up off the cobbles. 'I'm going to present it to the Commander-in-Chief!'

My dark mood was evaporating with every nautical mile we made up the Mediterranean. Mentally, I was forever urging the vessel forward, but her pace remained obstinately slow. The Government had forbidden ships returning from the Crimea to steam at full speed, so as to conserve coal—an article in extremely short supply. I felt in a state of suspended animation: there was nothing I could do, nothing to look forward to each day—there would be no more letters from my darling Sal. But, as compensation, neither had I to compose any more long reports for Lord Panmure: the War Office, I had quickly discovered, craved as much detail from me as ever had Edward Ladd Betts!

I tried to pass the time reading some of the books I had carefully brought from England with me, but the half-light in my cabin made it hard to concentrate on close print. Even my eyes started to ache, joining in the general rebellion of my body. In the end, I just kept plugging away at the last chapters of my story of the expedition.

We were still 250 miles from Malta when we met a gale—dead against us, slowing the ship still further. He would have to coal at Malta to avoid further delay. The captain saw no hope of us reaching Southampton until 15th December; maybe a couple of days more if there were to be rough weather through the Bay of Biscay.

I planned to stick with *Thames* all the way to England, thereby saving £20 and maybe deriving more benefit from the longer voyage. The alternative—changing at Malta to a French ship for Marseilles, then on by rail—was no journey to be undertaken without a servant; I doubted if I could have managed it anyway, in my present state.

I wrote to Sarah just before we left Malta telling her I expected to reach Southampton on or around 20th December and would telegraph her the moment we had docked.

* * * * * *

Never was grass greener than that in the fields bordering the Solent as we slipped slowly along, eager for every glimpse of the calm countryside—straight ploughed fields, trim hedgerows, winding lanes, settled hamlets with smoke rising from red chimneys. It took a good two hours for the ship to dock and for me to get off the all-important telegram to Sarah: 'I will be home on 24th December'.

On English soil again: a moment to savour! All noises were familiar ones; the scents, even those that were pungent, not in any way nauseous; the air soft, with just a hint of a recent shower. The streets were *clean*; not a cracked pavement in sight. My inn for the night was small but inviting. In the bar before dinner I drank a pint of Barclay and Perkins Entire straight off; afterwards, sprawled in a huge armchair, I smoked a cigar, watching sparks from the log fire vanish up the chimney.

Just before I went to sleep I remembered, quite inconsequentially, the gleam in Lord Stratford's eye when he caught sight of me while visiting Lord Raglan in April. 'Ah, Mr. Beatty,' he called out: 'You *did* follow your stars!' The remark puzzled the ADCs who were seeking to dissuade him from a second tour of the advanced trenches to see 'more action': only the day before, a Russian sniper's bullet had narrowly missed his head.

21

THE END OF A DREAM

11th March 1856

During the slow drive from the station to Blomfield Terrace I stared through the cab window, only half-believing in the reality of the massed ranks of buildings we were passing between, the thunder of the traffic, the lurid haze of the smoke-filled air.

I reached our front door, and knocked. How many times, I wondered, had Sarah approached that very door of a morning, hoping to find on the mat a letter from me. She opened it herself, and we were in each other's arms—laughing, crying, talking all at once. She drew me inside in her loving way: 'Henry'll look after your baggage,' she said. 'He insisted on coming over from Enniskillen with your brother William for Christmas—and you've just made it!'

The parlour was full of people but I had eyes only for my three children, standing shyly together at the front of the group. The tallest couldn't be, *must* be Fanny; how she had shot up but, oh, how thin! Red-haired Susy, almost up to her shoulder, looked bonny—and there was three-year-old Wallace, standing up straight and as manly as he knew how. I was on my knees in a second, my arms round them all. They were trembling with excitement, but speechless. I stood up: I had quite forgotten my red beard and whiskers! Though I had trimmed them carefully on the ship, they must have given the children a great fright, especially the two girls who would remember—if at all—only a clean-shaven Papa.

My sweet Sal saved me from further embarrassment. 'This is Eliza,' she said, 'and here is our Henry James.' I looked down at the tiny figure Eliza held gently in a shawl—our seven-month-old second boy, Henry James, fast asleep... 'He has only this minute dropped off after his feed. You'll see presently his eyes are the same colour as yours.'

I knew I had been right to take such a shine to Eliza Bernard if even only through letters—a dependable, no-nonsense young woman if ever there was one, but kindly and with a twinkle in her eye which now looked suspiciously like a tear. 'Thank you, Eliza,' I said, 'for being such a tower of strength.'

'I wasn't the only one,' she replied shyly, 'Mary has been helping me the last two months.' And there beside her was Mary Burke, Sal's younger sister, looking not a day older than when I had last seen her as a bridesmaid at our wedding twelve years before. Henry pounced on me, clapping my shoulder and babbling at the top of his voice before dashing off to deal with the cabby and my pile of travel-battered luggage on the pavement. William, whom I hadn't seen for so long, clasped both my hands in an almighty grip, 'Welcome home, Jim,' he said. 'It's good to see you safe and sound; sorry I was such a poor letter-writer, but you know how it is.' Nothing mattered but that he had come over from our old home to greet me on my return. 'Stay for a bit this time, William,' I said. 'We've much to tell each other.' He nodded gravely.

Christmas Eve supper at No. 13 was boisterous—no, it was downright rowdy; everyone wanted to talk or shout at the same time. During the evening, Henry insisted on having his musical moment, as he called it, and sang two ballads in his piercing, slightly erratic tenor voice. Then my two girls gave us their duet, which, said Eliza, they had been secretly practising for weeks. Imagine my reaction when they piped up with *Cheer, boys, cheer!* After that, but only after they had demanded nuts and sweetmeats—'same as the grown-ups'—they were whisked off to bed by Eliza and Mary, with my promise to come and kiss all three when they were in bed.

'You've got them that dizzy, Jim, they'll not sleep tonight, the same as the rest of us,' said Sal tenderly.

'Just once in a lifetime, my darling; how often does a father come back from war to such a wonderful scene? Remember our last Christmas?' I could see by her face that the memory was still painful. 'Never mind,' I said, trying to distract her, 'I did finally manage to open the hat box you sent out, even though you didn't include the key!'

This released smiles and tears, and we spent the rest of a long evening in reminiscence—William silently approving everything said but speaking little. Henry grew more voluble as the hours went by, and had to be cut short by his sister! Looking at her radiant face and feeling her soft hand in mine, I certainly felt I had successfully come through all my trials and perils: I could almost persuade myself that her mere presence would be sufficient to cure all of my petty ills.

Business as usual was no motto for a Beatty Christmas Day, though I did start it off with a flourish by shaving off beard and moustache and soaking long in a bath. After that, the children and the women took over: there seemed to be non-stop baking and roasting and laughter in the kitchen. I was showered with presents—from little Wallace, a highly recognisable drawing of a locomotive with a funnel so tall as to defy gravity; a veritable bevy of coloured paper angels fashioned by the girls. Henry came across with a handsome box of cigars; and from William, a wholly unexpected gift—a diary belonging to our father, covering all the events of his long years in Enniskillen. On the last page was a pencil sketch by a friend showing the Old Doctor in his Militia uniform, standing beside his trap. Gifts of slippers and socks came from practical Eliza and Mary; and there was a handsome green velvet waistcoat from my beloved.

'I didn't quite know what size to make it,' she confessed. 'I was so relieved when I got your letter saying how little your weight had altered.' I put it on then and there: it fitted me a treat.

'But you're much too skinny, Jim, and the left side of your face is all red.' She patted my cheek: it felt tender to the touch.

'The result of rough shaving, that's all,' I replied breezily. 'That particular bit of skin hasn't seen the light of day for nearly twelve months.'

Sal had got presents for everyone, but I had nothing to contribute. Then I remembered the peddler who had followed me halfway up the gangway as I was boarding *Thames*, thrusting fluttering scarves at me. I had bought three, more to get rid of him than for any other reason. Now I fished them out of my valise upstairs and brought them down, along with a handful of coat buttons I had picked up on the battlefield of Inkerman and on the trampled meadows at Traktir Bridge. Wallace was overjoyed with those, and promptly retreated under the table to arrange and rearrange his precious new hoard. Sarah, Fanny and Susy pronounced themselves delighted with the scarves, draping them in dashing style round their shoulders, and pirouetting round the room in what they judged was true Middle Eastern fashion. The colours were certainly more startling than I had remembered when I bought them in the gloom of that Balaklava afternoon, with snow thickening by the minute, but their garish designs somehow matched the festive mood.

I gave Henry a crust of grey Russian bread I had found in the street in Sebastopol, 'for Auld Lang Syne', which he seemed to appreciate as a gesture. All poor William got was an old cap—'my *lucky* cap' I insisted, that I had worn at work most days. It had even survived my headlong fall from the wagon near the Col in September. Mary and Eliza were just given a heartfelt kiss apiece!

Neighbours and their children called during the day to welcome back 'the stranger' and stayed for sherry and home-made mince pies—much more tasty than those of Mother Seacole, I told Sarah. Yet, for some reason, I found some difficulty in swallowing, and nothing could shift my headache.

The pain, as well as the excitement, kept me wakeful that night, and was still in evidence on Boxing day morning. Thinking that a brisk walk would clear my head, we set off *en famille*, the air mild but with a little wind, the two girls grand in their bright Chersonese scarves. After lunch, I lay back in my armchair, trying to find a position where the throbbing was lessened. At once, the girls clambered into my lap, little Wallace at my knee. 'Tell us, Papa,' said Fanny, 'what was it really like out there in the Crimea?' 'Did you see snakes?' asked Susy. 'What are Russians?' That question came from Wallace. I was at a loss: in what words could I convey to my children anything of all I had seen and heard—the girls with their bright scarves and brighter eyes, my son solemnly clutching Russian buttons in his tiny hands? I felt totally engulfed still in the immense tragedy and suffering and folly of that war, of which I had in a way become a part and to which I would soon be returning. All the ambitions and dreams of early days had sharpened strangely to that single focus.

All at once I began remembering ridiculous things: Bill the Barber writing his patriotic ode; the way the chicks' mother had started using red ink for her letters and how the colour had run so much I couldn't read her writing; how I had sawn a salt-beef barrel in half to make tubs for Campbell and myself. Then another picture came to my mind, and I told them the story of the bos'un and the mule.

'This little mule,' I began, 'had come to Balaklava with many companions all the way from Sardinia on a boat with soldiers. The weather had been rough, and he was badly injured. They thought he was dying and left him near the harbour. Soon after, a boatswain from HMS *Rodney*, a Mr. Collins, passed by on his way to the naval dockyard where his men were working. He lifted up the mule's head and gave him water to drink; later he brought him food. After several days the little mule gradually started to crawl; finally he stood up, his wounds healed and he grew sleek and strong again. From then on, he followed Mr. Collins about just like a dog, in and out of the huts and among the sailors, wherever the boatswain's business took him.'

That was acclaimed a capital story. 'What was the mule's name?' 'Monty,' I replied promptly, 'because the soldiers came from Piedmont.' So I had to tell that story again, with Monty's name in that time. 'I wish I had a mule like Monty,' said Wallace. 'Silly, your legs are far too short to sit astride on,' said Nan-Nan. 'What happened to the little mule in the end?' asked tender-hearted Susy. 'I don't know,' I replied. 'I had to leave Balaklava. I expect Mr. Collins has found him a home: he would, I know, be welcomed by Mrs. Seacole, the lady who owns the British Hotel.'

That satisfied the chicks. I heard them relating the story in the kitchen—several times over, in fact. Sarah came in with a telegram: 'It's from Sir Morton Peto—he wants to come tomorrow afternoon to see you,' she announced. 'He looked in once or twice while you were away. And here's a letter from Mr. Betts—I think it's from him. It arrived before Christmas, but I must have mislaid it in all the excitement.'

I, too, knew Betts' handwriting well—too well, perhaps. The letter had been written from his club; it was as always brief and to the point.

Dear Beatty

    By the time you read this I shall be in Montreal—
the Trans-Canadian route is going great guns again,
just as you and I thought it would. Welcome home:
get fit soon! I'll see you in the Spring.

    Thanks for all your work; you've done us proud.
My best regards to Mrs. B.

    Cordially

    Edward Ladd Betts.

    PS. Your young Henry James is a corker, by all
accounts. Congratulations!

'Before Sir Morton comes I want Dr. Clarke to examine you,' said Sarah. 'You're not your old self at all—I'm dreadful worried about you, Jim.' To satisfy her I suggested she made an appointment for the next morning. He arrived promptly at 11 am and greeted me cordially—Sal had been scrupulous in settling his accounts in good time!

He asked me to strip and lie on the bed; he then gave me a thorough examination—checking reflexes, listening with his stethoscope, peering into my ears, feeling carefully round my neck. 'It's a mystery,' he said while I slipped my clothes on. 'Your heart appears sound, your lungs, too. Though your neck is slightly swollen I can find no obstruction in your throat to account for difficulty in swallowing. Though you are thin, I would not describe it as clinical emaciation. As for your eyes, they appear a trifle bloodshot—maybe a belated tribute to the Christmas spirit!' After that somewhat laboured attempt at humour Dr. Clarke reverted to his normal professional manner. 'I shall prescribe some pills to quieten you: but remember, you've come through an exceedingly strenuous and harassing time. You *must* rest all you can—no work or exertion of any kind for the present. And not too many callers: they tend to stir the brain to over-activity.'

Lying back on the bed, I thought over his remarks. The next thing I knew Sarah was gently waking me for lunch! Sir Morton's visit in the afternoon was not, as it happened, stressful at all. From a man of his natural reserve his praise for my work sounded almost fulsome—embarrassing, really. He said that all the directors felt that pledges to Lord Aberdeen had been more than fulfilled: the expedition had been a resounding success. Both he and Lord Panmure were agreed on that—and the Secretary of State for War had hinted at greater responsibilities for me when properly recovered. 'Full health, and speedily, that is my earnest prayer for you, my dear Beatty.' Sir Morton's voice shook as he uttered those words, but his hand-shake on parting was as firm and decisive as ever. 'I know I leave you in the very best of hands,' he remarked, bowing slightly to Sarah. 'You are lucky; your wife is a treasure, if I may say so.'

That was quite enough excitement for one day. I turned in early and tried vainly to find peace from my pain with rest, as prescribed.

But at the start of the New Year I began to feel more my old self again and able to tackle our financial affairs that had been put into a terrible pickle through Camidge's devious practices. I brought a blush to Sarah's face by complimenting her on the spirited way in which she had handled family and other problems in my absence. 'I was relieved to find that I was able to deal with those men you dismissed,' she said. 'I sent them on their way to Great George Street without too much bitterness on their part. Honestly, in their hearts I don't think they blamed you for their troubles—and some of their wives were good souls.'

Steinhauser and his two unmarried sisters came one afternoon for what proved to be a much extended tea-party. Adolphus looked every inch the prosperous railway company director he was, but under that bland exterior was, I knew, a very warm feeling for the Beatty family and its fortunes. The three of them agreed that Sarah's long spell in Brighton with the children had been beneficial; any place was, they declared, a welcome change from the fogs and fevers of London. Fanny was a quite restored little girl.

A long letter arrived from Donald—the first in what turned out to be a weekly series, keeping me informed of every development on the railway. Doyne and his men were making a fair fist on the track maintenance side; his new all-weather road had followed our route for almost its entire length! Donald added that Doyne was having even more trouble in disciplining his men than we had had with our navvies. Well, I thought, he would have to evolve his own methods of control: that was Donald's view, too. HQ, he reported, was greatly changed in personnel, and much subdued: the prospect of tackling the Russians all over again in the spring was exercising every mind. Half the Navy had sailed or was steaming for home. 'General Rumour' had it that there were to be negotiations for an armistice. He wished us all a Happy New Year, and sent greetings from Henry Stone and Mrs. Seacole. Also, a PS to report that the temperature had dropped 45°F in the previous 24 hours.

A racking pain in my head, combined with surprisingly red eyes and—for the first time—some spectacular wheezing, drove me back under the covers for a day or two.

So passed January and the early part of February. The children no longer found it odd to have a father who spent so much time in bed and mostly insisted on being left alone. Whenever I rallied, they made my bed their playroom—paper and crayons all over the coverlet, mixed up with toys and Wallace's infernal buttons that would keep slipping down between the sheets.

By now I had quite a fund of suitable stories. The chicks were tickled by the notion of the tired commissariat camel that fell asleep directly outside Russell's hut door, thus preventing it from being opened. 'Why didn't he climb out of the window?' 'It was too small and Mr. Russell was too big.' They marvelled at the strangeness of the Crimea itself—its mud, its snow, its hurricanes, its drifts of wild flowers, its eagles and flocks of unknown waterfowl. But they drew the line at any mention of centipedes and bugs. Quite right, too, I thought: their judgment matched with mine.

Bill the Barber always fascinated them: a special favourite was the tale of him painting name boards for the navvies' huts. 'Why can't our house have a name, Papa, and not just horrid No. 13?' demanded Nan-Nan.

One dark morning at the beginning of February, Sal brought in her cherished scrapbook: 'I've pasted in all the cuttings from *The Times* about your railway, right from the start,' she said, putting it into

223

my hands. 'But I'm proudest of this last one you wouldn't have seen: it was only published here after you had already left Balaklava.'

A double border in red surrounded the cutting:

> *Mr. Beatty goes home immediately, if indeed, he has not already gone, and I much regret that he has been obliged to retire from a post in which he rendered services not only to the army collectively, but to many individuals in it, who will always retain a deep sense of his kindness and friendly assistance in times of domestic difficulty about huts and transports.*

'Your Mr. Russell is a really nice gentleman,' said Sarah fondly.

Idly, I leafed through the pages. On one, Sal had copied out a short prayer; opposite was the envelope of my first letter home from the Crimea—amazingly uncreased. A lock of Susy's hair lay on top.

'That's quite enough, Jim,' said Sarah reprovingly. 'It's *my* scrapbook: I began it the day I first met you nine years ago.'

By this time, Dr. Clarke had become a more regular visitor. He had now got me sitting propped up in bed to make breathing easier at night. I was conscious of a growing hoarseness when speaking. William was an unexpected support, prepared to sit with me for hours, sometimes in companionable silence, at others—uncharacteristically—recalling at length shared boyhood memories. He spoke of George Stone, who was now living at Ballinlanders, Co. Tipperary. I remembered him vividly as a plucky young boxer with whom I had often been in competition for the Enniskillen Belt. Always our talk seemed to slip back into the past... The news in Donald's letters seemed to be coming from a country even more remote.

I was still working slowly—so slowly—on the last pages of my story of the expedition: even with the lightest of pencils it was painful work, and words straggled untidily across the sheets. At last, it was done!

I had to ask Sarah to take over writing all letters—even to Donald—at my dictation. The first time we tried it out, she burst into tears, poor sweet lamb.

Everything changed radically after the visit of Dr. Clarke and his specialist colleague on 18th February, and their fateful diagnosis: aneurysm of the aorta.

There was little time left. Sarah took command of all business affairs. I made a will: for the last time I used the signature that had appeared at the bottom of so many paysheets and reports in the Crimea. No self-pity; only the heartbreak of knowing I would never be sharing with my beloved the joy of seeing our chicks grow up and flourish.

We had begun to pray together again, and Sarah would read aloud to me—often from the Psalms, and her favourite, No. 40:

> *I waited patiently for the Lord; and he inclined unto me, and heard my cry. He brought me up also out of an horrible pit, out of the miry clay, and set my feet upon the rock, and established my goings. Blessed is that man that maketh the Lord his trust, and respecteth not the proud nor such as turn aside to lies.*

My arms are unbearably swollen.
Sal stroked my heated face: she's fetching a cold compress—

* * * * * *

As I came back into our bedroom, Jim was in terrible convulsions, then he slumped sideways, unconscious. I felt for his pulse. It had gone.

Everything in the room was still.

The end of our bright dream.

Sarah Jane Beatty
11th March 1856

AFTERWORD

James Beatty did not live to enjoy the final triumph of his railway in the Crimea. He died, after months of suffering, on 11th March 1856 at his home, 13 Blomfield Terrace, Paddington, London, while details of the Allied/Russian Peace Treaty were still being worked out in Paris. The cause of death was aneurism of the aorta, brought on by internal injuries sustained during an accident at the front. He was thirty-five years old.

The Crimean War lives in British memory as a cataclysmic campaign, which was mitigated only by the valour of the ordinary soldier. Never to be forgotten—or forgiven—was the paralysing muddle, the crass mishandling of resources by the generals. In all the three years, disaster never taught a single lesson at the top. The same blindness characterised the Peace Conference: there was hardly any mention of the causes for which the war had ostensibly been fought; no new guidelines for Europe's future. Britain's military establishment was shown to be deeply flawed, and emerged with a shattered structure. This did not prevent honours and promotions—as usual—being awarded to the leaders.

But, for Beatty, the engineer-in-chief of the Civil Engineering Corps in the Crimea and the instrument of final victory, there was no public recognition of his unique achievement. Even at the time his contribution attracted little attention, and to this day it is still largely unknown or undervalued. Shortly after his death, however, one personal tribute was paid him by his colleagues in that great railway enterprise—Sir Morton Peto, Bt., Mr. Thomas Brassey and Mr. Edward Betts, partners in the famous contracting firm of Peto, Brassey & Betts (PB&B) which Beatty had served with such distinction during the last years of his short professional life.

Over his tomb at Kensal Green Cemetery these three men placed an impressive monument. Its inscription expressed their

'esteem for the personal character of the deceased and their appreciation of the valuable services rendered by him to the nation in the construction of the railway in the Crimea'.

They knew at first hand the calibre of the man they were posthumously honouring. Something of the inner strength of his nature can be glimpsed in extracts from a letter to his wife, Sarah, by James on 9th January 1855, while in Constantinople, en route for the Crimea:

> *I am really anxious to get to Balaklava, and if it pleases God to enable me to mitigate the miseries of the finest Army that ever left England it will be a triumph indeed.*
> *... I trust to a Merciful God to give me health and strength to get through the labour and difficulties of my position, which I will not conceal from you are very great. In fact, I have got a responsibility that nothing but energy and perseverance will enable me to get through, with honour and advantage.*

Honours apart, the Crimean railway was Beatty's true monument. He would have been the first to savour the irony of his line's fate: the initial speed of its construction was matched only by the rapidity with which it was dismantled at the end of the war. In May 1856, Lord Stratford negotiated the sale of all rails and plant to the Turkish Government. Within days, 800 men of the British Army Works Corps began to pull up all the new miles of track. All movable material was sold off to a private company planning a new pilgrim railway. When the last British troops left Balaklava two months later, all traces of Beatty's historic railway had vanished.

Death put an end to any long-term financial plans he might have hoped to put in place for his family from whom he was so often separated. Some 70 letters written to his wife during his year in the Crimea bear testimony to his love and constant concern for them. At the time of his death, Sarah (his 'beloved Sal') was thirty-five. She was left with their four small children: Frances (Fanny), aged six; Susanna (Susy), four; Wallace, two; and Henry James, ten months.

During his latter days in the Crimea, Beatty had entertained sanguine hopes of continued Government employment there: Lord Panmure, the then Secretary of State for War, had personally urged him to stay on as chief engineer, and he would have done so had his health been equal to the task. Even had he, later, decided to continue his engineering career in a civilian field he could have looked confidently forward to success on an international scale, similar to that enjoyed by his old pupil-master Woodhouse and several of his peers. None of this was to be.

An event then occurred that would mightily have eased his mind. Through the good offices of Sir Morton Peto and the Duke of Newcastle, Sarah Beatty was granted a Government pension of £100 per annum, equivalent to that for the widow of 'a full colonel falling in the field'.

James—Jim to his family and intimates—was born in Enniskillen, Co. Fermanagh, Ireland, on 31st March 1820, the elder son of Dr. James Beatty and his wife Susanna (nee Renwick). She died tragically, aged thirty-two, in 1826 when Jim was just six years old. Dr. Beatty (the Old Doctor), who had gained his MD at Edinburgh University in 1808, was a notable figure in Enniskillen where he practised until his retirement in 1853. He was superintendent of the cholera hospital in 1832 during the epidemic, and was also assistant surgeon to the Enniskillen Militia.

At Mr. Hugh McIver's private academy in Enniskillen, James studied English, mensuration, trigonometry and surveying; at home, his father taught him the classics. Struck by his son's talents in construction and mathematics, he determined a career for him as a civil engineer. At the age of fifteen, James became a pupil of Mr. T.J. Woodhouse, MICE, the new resident engineer of the Midland Counties Railway, then in the course of construction. James so impressed him that, at the end of his pupillage, he made him an assistant engineer on the line. In 1840 James was employed in surveying the Manchester and Derby Line.

Two years later he joined the contracting firm of Peto and Betts on the Norwich, Brandon and Lowestoft lines; in 1845 he was appointed their chief engineer in charge of works on the Southampton-Dorchester Railway.

He married Sarah Jane Burke, eldest daughter of Revd. Henry Anthony Burke, rector of Magheracross, Enniskillen, and his wife Julia Frances (*née* Blake) on 21st November 1849.

Beatty had his first taste of work overseas in the summer of 1852, by which time he had been elected an associate member of the Institution of Civil Engineers. Peto and Betts commissioned him to explore and lay out the European and North American Railway in New Brunswick. This was to be one of the key links in a chain of railways designed to connect Halifax, the nearest port to England, with the innermost recesses of Canada and the United States. On his staff, and appointed by Joseph Locke, MP, the distinguished engineer, was Donald Campbell who was to become a friend and trusted colleague for the rest of Beatty's life.

Some indication of the difficulties that had to be grappled with in Canada was given in a memoir of Beatty, published after his death by the ICE:

> *On arrival at St John's, there only remained about three months in which to make the necessary sections, etc. the greater part being through primaeval forest. However, owing to Mr Beatty's great energy and incredible exertions, trial sections were taken in every direction. Permanent surveys and estimates of the works were also so advanced as to enable the contract for the portion from St John's to Shediac to be made between the New Brunswick Government and Messrs. Peto and Betts.*

James then returned to England; in the following spring he was appointed engineer-in-chief of the New Brunswick Railways. However, on the eve of sailing, the firm suddenly altered his destination to Nova Scotia, giving him the task of exploring and laying out all the routes in that province for the projected system of Canadian Railways.

The ICE memoir paints a vivid picture of the arduous working conditions Beatty encountered:

> *As in New Brunswick, the surveys had to be made through dense forest. The surveying parties literally cut their*

way—often felling within 20 or 30 yards half-a-dozen splendid trees. By Christmas, trial sections had been taken all over the country, the line was surveyed and permanently staked out over the whole of the route from Halifax to Truro, and from thence by two routes, one around and the other across the Cobequid Mountains, to the New Brunswick frontier, as well as branches from Halifax to Windsor, the direct route to St John's, New Brunswick and from Truro to Pictou, the route towards Prince Edward Island. During the whole of this period the various parties had been camping out, living in the woods with a thin canvas single tent for covering, salt pork and hard biscuit for provisions, and for the last month three feet of snow on the ground, with the thermometer down to 15 degrees below zero, Mr. Beatty was continually moving from party to party, encouraging and stimulating all to the greatest exertion by his own example, and taking his share of hardships of the situation.

Growing uncertainty about the political outlook in Europe brought progress in Canada to an abrupt halt. Beatty and his staff returned to England from Halifax in February 1854. With him sailed Sarah, the two little girls and three-month-old Wallace.

After James' death in March, 1856, Sarah's family persuaded her to move to Ireland with the four small children, to be nearer them. She settled outside Dublin, where she lived for the next thirty-two years until her death in 1888. Her father, Revd. Henry Burke, not only officiated at her marriage to James in 1849, but two years earlier had married Michael, her eldest brother, and Lizzie, James' younger sister. Sarah's mother, Julia Frances, had six children in all. Henry, her elder son, accompanied James to the Crimea as an assistant surveyor; they became close companions.

Wallace, Beatty's elder son (1853–1923), took after his paternal grandfather in pursuing a career in medicine. He entered Trinity College, Dublin, becoming a royal, classical and medical scholar, and gaining his MD in 1886. He had a distinguished medical career, and was elected a member of the Royal Academy of Medicine. In 1888 he married Frances Eleanor (Fenella), daughter of Dr Samuel and Mary Edge. They had four sons: Wallace, who died unmarried, aged twenty-one; Henry, who became a judge in the Indian Civil Service; Eric, who was killed in action in 1915; Dr John, MD, a GP in Swallowfield, Reading, from 1929 until his death in 1984; and Desmond, who became chairman of Irish Raleigh Industries, and died in 1967.

Henry James, the second son (born 1855) followed in his father's profession, obtaining an engineering degree from Trinity College, Dublin. He emigrated to Australia where he became an engineer on the Queensland Railway.

Frances (Fanny), James' first-born daughter, died unmarried in 1873, aged twenty-two, after suffering years of illness since childhood.

Susanna (Susy), the younger girl, was married on 8th February 1877, aged twenty-five, to Roger Casement, DL, eldest son of John Casement, JP, MA, and his wife Charlotte, of Magherintemple, Co. Antrim.

Roger and Susy had five sons: John (1880–1944) became a Captain, RN; Francis (1881–1967) a Major-General, RAMC; Roger Hugh (1883–1924), Robert James (1884–1946) and Reginald (1886–1962) became railway engineers.

Sarah, James Beatty's widow, died on 4th February 1888, aged sixty-seven.

ACKNOWLEDGMENTS

I am indebted to many individuals and institutions for generous help and encouragement during the researching and writing of this book.

A special debt of gratitude is owed to Major Colin Robins, OBE, RA (retd), of the Crimean War Research Society, noted military commentator on the campaign, and to Brian Cooke CEngMMechE, author of *The Grand Crimean Central Railway*, both of whom have kindly read my manuscript. Their shrewd technical comments on various points of the narrative have enabled me to strengthen its authenticity and avoid error: their warm support has been much appreciated. I am also grateful to Dr. Nicola Kirk, MB FRCPath; Peter Sambrook, MSc and Peter Moon.

I am glad to acknowledge permission from the Deputy Keeper of the Records, Public Record Office of Northern Ireland and to Mrs. A. Casement to publish extracts from MIC 166.

I have received valuable assistance from the Institution of Civil Engineers (particularly from Mary Murphy, ALA, the archivist, and Carol Arrowsmith); Francis Herbert, Curator of Maps, Royal Geographical Society; Michael Robbins, author of *The Balaklava Railway*; Aiden Flood, Camden Local History Museum; J.B. Cahill, Archivist, Public Archives of Nova Scotia; Bob Gilmore, Provincial Archives of New Brunswick; Dr Peter Boyden and reading-room staff, National Army Museum; London Library; Victoria Library; and the Public Record Office at Kew and Chancery Lane.

I am greatly indebted for advice and assistance to: Sir Henry Peto Bt.; Wallace Beatty; Mrs. Lesley Casement and Hugh Casement; Séamas MacAnnaidh, Irish author and historian; and Dr. G.D. Sheffield, RMC, Sandhurst. Also to: Patricia Smith; Keith Elliott, head of PMA; Pete Yeo, FMK Solutions; George and Gwyneth Walker; Rev. Dr. E.C. Brooks; Gordon Cradock; Hilary Carrington; Polly Willis; Kathleen Carroll; Joanna Mack, Domino Films; Conrad Voss-Bark; Stephen Rose; and Geoffrey Skelton, for unfailing support and wise counsel.

I should like to thank Professor Andrew Lambert, King's College, London; Patricia Kernaghan, Public Record Office, Belfast; Frances Dimond, Curator, Royal Archives Photograph Collection; Malvin Van Gelderen who designed the cover; Patricia Collins, Manchester Arts Library; Mark Abbott, Science and Society; David Mowat, publisher; my family and all my many friends and ex-colleagues for their generous help and encouragement.

I must also thank the *Illustrated London News; The Times*; *Punch* Library; Terry Coleman, author of *The Railway Navvies*; R.K. Middlemas, author of *The Master Builders*; Alex Attewell, Curator, Florence Nightingale Museum; and H. & A. Gernsheim, authors of *Roger Fenton*.

Lastly, my thanks to Jane, my wife, for her acute insights, wholehearted collaboration and loving patience.

ILLUSTRATIONS

Plate 1, portrait of James Beatty MICE, is reproduced by kind permission of Wallace Beatty, great-grandson; Plates 2 and 3 are reproduced by permission of the Science Museum/*Science and Society*; Plate 4 is reproduced by courtesy of Lady Peto; Plates 5, 6, 7, 9, 10, 11, 17, 18 and 19 are reproduced by permission of *The Illustrated London News* Picture Library; Plates 8, 13 and 15 are reproduced by permission of The Royal Archives © 1999 Her Majesty the Queen; Plate 14 is reproduced from a National Army Museum postcard by W.J. Colville; Plate 16 is reproduced by permission of The National Portrait Gallery; Plates 12 and 20 are reproduced by permission of Manchester Central Library; line drawing by Karen Humpage of James Beatty's chest tomb is reproduced courtesy of Friends of Kensal Green Cemetery; Plate 21 is reproduced by permission of the Public Record Office, Kew.

SOURCES

British Library
Camden Library
Edinburgh University Library
Enniskillen Library
General Register Office, Belfast
Guildhall Library
Holborn Library
House of Lords Record Office
Institution of Civil Engineers
Irish Medical Council
London Library
Manchester Central Library
National Army Museum
National Portrait Gallery
National Library of Ireland, Dublin
National Railway Museum
Paddington Library
Probate Register
Provincial Archives of Nova Scotia
Public Record Office, Chancery Lane
Public Record Office, Kew
Public Record office of Northern Ireland
Register General's Office, Dublin
Science Museum
Trinity College Library, Dublin

PRIVATELY PRINTED

Cooke, B. *The Grand Crimean Central Railway* (1990)
Chown, J.L. *Sir Morton Peto*
Neilson, Mrs A. *The Crimea, Its Town, Inhabitants and Social Customs*

Peto, Sir H. *Sir Morton Peto, a Memorial Sketch* (1892)
Robins, Major C. *The Murder of a Regiment: Written Sketches from the Crimea 1854–1855* (1994)
Smith, Patricia: Thesis

NEWSPAPERS AND PERIODICALS

Enniskillen Chronicle and Erne Pacquet
Fermanagh Mail
Fermanagh Sentinel
Illustrated London News (1854–56)
Impartial Reporter & Farmers' Journal
Journal of Transport History
The Times (1854–56)
Punch

PRINTED

Adye, J. *Review of the Crimean War* (1860)
Airlie, Countess of. *With the Guards We Shall Go* (1933)
Anglesey, Earl of. *Little Hodge* (1971)
Baring Pemberton, W. *Battles of the Crimean War* (1962)
Barker, A.J. *The Vainglorious War*
Boase, G. *Modern English Biography* (1892)
Bonham-Carter, Dr G. *Camp Life as Seen by a Civilian* (1871)
Brassey, T. *Work and Wages* (1972)
Bushby, H.J. *A Month in the Camp Before Sebastopol* (1855)
Calthorpe, S.J.G. *Letters from Headquarters* (1856)
Cambridge Modern History (1830–70)
Campbell, C.F. *Letters from Camp* (1894)
Carter, E.F. *Railways in Wartime* (1964)
Chapman, C. *Russell of The Times*
Chesney, K. *Crimean War Reader* (1960)
Chrimes, M. *Civil Engineering 1839–89: A Photographic History* (1991)
Clifford, H. *Letters and Sketches from the Crimea* (1956)

Henry Clifford, V.C. (1871)

Coleman, T. *The Railway Navvies* (1965)

Compton, P. *Colonel's Lady and Camp Follower* (1970)

Cooke, E.T. *Life of Florence Nightingale* (1913)

Dictionary of National Biography

Dodd, G. *Pictorial History of the Russian War* (1854–56)

Duberly, Mrs H. *Journal Kept During Russian War* (1855)

Evelyn, G.P. *A Diary of the Crimea* (1954)

Fenwick, K. (ed). *A Voice from the Ranks* (1954)

Franks, H. *Leaves from a Soldier's Notebook* (1904)

Gernsheim, H. & A. *Roger Fenton: Photographer of the Crimean War* (1955)

Gibbs, P. *Crimean Blunders* (1960)

Godfrey, A.W. *Crimea Diary*

Hannavy, J. *The Camera Goes to War* (1974)

Hansard (1855–57)

Harris, J. *The Gallant Six Hundred* (1973)

Harrison, Sir G.W. *71 Years of a Guardsman's Life* (1916)

Heath, L.G. *Letters from the Black Sea* (1897)

Helps, Sir A. *Life and Labours of Mr Brassey* (1872)

Hibbert, C. *Destruction of Lord Raglan in the Crimea* (1984)

Kingslake, A.W. *The Invasion of the Crimea* (1887)

A Lady Volunteer: *Eastern Hospitals and English Nurses* (1856)

Lambert, A. *The Crimean War* (1887)

Lambert, R. *The Railway King*

Letters from the Crimea, A Story of Active Service (1886)

MacMunn, Sir G. *Crimean Perspective* (1935)

Martineau, J. *Life of Henry Pelham, Fifth Duke of Newcastle* (1908)

Middlemas, R.K. *The Master Builders* (1963)

Nolan, E.H. *Illustrated History of the War Against Russia* (1857)

Oxford History of England 1815–1870

Paget, Lord George. *The Light Brigade in the Crimea* (1881)

Parliamentary Papers, Selected (1854–57)

Portal, R. *Letters from the Crimea*

Porter, Major-General W. *History of the Corps of Royal Engineers* (1951)

Ransom, P.J.G. *The Victorian Railway and How It Evolved* (1990)

Robbins, M. *The Balaklava Railway* (1953)

Russell, W.H. *The War in the Crimea* (1855–56)

_____*Dispatches from the Crimea*

_____*The Great War with Russia* (1895)

Simmons, Professor Jack. *The Railway in England and Wales 1830–1914* (1978)

Simpson, W. *Autobiography* (1903)

_____*The Seat of the War* (1855)

Skene, J.H. *With Lord Stratford in the Crimean War* (1883)

Soyer, A. *Soyer's Culinary Operations* (1857)

Sterling, A. *Story of the Highland Brigade* (1895)

Sweetman, J. *Raglan, from the Peninsula to the Crimea*

Tisdall, E.E.P. *Mrs Duberly's Campaign* (1963)

Whishaw, F. *Railways of Great Britain and Ireland* (1845)

Windham, Sir C.A. *Crimean Diary and Letters* (1897)

Woodham-Smith, C. *The Reason Why* (1853)

Wrottesley, G. *Life and Correspondence of Sir John Burgoyne* (1873)

Wyld, J. *Coasts and Ports of the Black Sea* (1854)